THE ULTIMATE WEIGHT TRAINING JOURNAL

A ONE YEAR PERSONAL TRAINING
JOURNAL & FITNESS GUIDE

MICHAEL JESPERSEN

P9-BQJ-682

REVISED EDITION

Third Printing

• *PRODUCTIVE FITNESS PRODUCTS* •

The Ultimate Weight Training Journal

A One Year Personal Training Journal & Fitness Guide

By Mike Jespersen

Published by:

Productive Fitness Products
P.O. Box 2325
Blaine, WA 98231-2325
U.S.A.

Visit our Website: www.productivefitness.com

International Standard Book Number: 0-9696773-2-4
Printed and Bound in Canada

For quantity discounts please write:

Productive Fitness Products
P.O. Box 2325
Blaine, WA 98231-2325
U.S.A.
e-mail: mike@productivefitness.com
or call toll free: 1-888-221-8833

Productive Fitness Products

Writing & Research
Michael Jespersen
Harry Wasylyk
Dr. Alan Vernec
Scott Livingston
Nikos Apostolopoulos

Editors
Dr. Alan Vernec
Scott Livingston
Kristina Bischoff
Keith Waddington
Linda Jespersen

Photography
Fotofolio
Scarabee Productions
Michael Jespersen
Marie Deruaz

Contributors
Yahoo Productions
RDM Sales
Myles Lorenson

Publisher
Productive Fitness
Products
P.O. Box 2325
Blaine, Washington
98231-2325

Canadian address:
Productive Fitness
Products
1774-140 St.
Surrey, BC
V4A 4G9

Table of Contents

FOREWORD

There are two important points we would like to emphasize before you begin reading this publication. Firstly, The Ultimate Weight Training Journal was created for both men and women (of all ages), however it was written in the masculine tense for simplicity. Secondly, although we use the term "weight training" it should be understood this includes all aspects of resistance training such as weight lifting, bodybuilding, body toning, etc.. Weight training is, without a doubt, the best way of increasing strength, while shaping and toning your body.

GUARANTEED RESULTS !!

We are so certain that the results you can achieve using this book will meet and even surpass your expectations that we offer this unprecedented "Double your Money Back Guarantee". If after one year from starting the Training Log while following the principles outlined in this book, mainly;

- fill out a log page for each workout, for the period of one year, while always striving for improvement.
- follow a principle of sound nutrition, using the *Nutrition Optimizer* as a guide.
- do a minimum of 3 aerobic sessions per week (for minimum of 20 minutes each).
- allow 48 hours rest for muscle groups worked after weight training sessions.,

you are not completely satisfied with the results you see and feel we will refund double the purchase price of *The Ultimate Weight Training Journal* to you.

Productive Fitness Products
P.O. Box 2325
Blaine, WA 98231-2325

Please send the original copy of your receipt (make a photocopy for yourself) and your filled copy of *The Ultimate Weight Training Journal* with a note giving your name, sex, age, phone number, and address with a short note telling us what your goal was and we will send you double your money back. Remember our goal is to help you reach your goal.

INTRODUCTION

Weight training is no longer an exclusive activity for bodybuilders and athletes. Today, weight training is a practical means for people of all ages and both sexes to stay fit and strong. The benefits from weight training include increased strength, improved body image, stronger bones, faster metabolism, improved lymphatic drainage, and increased self confidence.

The Ultimate Weight Training Journal combines the three most fundamental elements in attaining overall health and fitness: anaerobic training (weight training), aerobic training and proper nutrition. The information provided will help you choose and implement an appropriate training routine, as well as, explain nutrition basics. Moreover, your Training Log entries will allow you to make gradual and consistent improvements in each workout. The *Nutrition Optimizer* is used to evaluate and adjust your diet to meet your specific requirements. The Ultimate Weight Training Journal will soon have you "Training smart". This means focusing on achieving your goals in an intelligent manner, avoiding wasted time and energy.

To the beginner:

If you are a beginner this book is of special importance. Changes in your physical appearance take time and often are not immediately apparent. Long before you experience noticeable changes in the size and tone of your muscles, you will notice changes in your level of strength. These changes will be apparent by your entries in the Training Log. In addition, by recording your workout sessions, nutritional intake, body measurements and weight, you will acquire an understanding of how your body reacts to both training and nutritional variations, learning what works best for you. We hope this realization will encourage you to continue training.

Good Luck !

BODY
DIAGRAMS

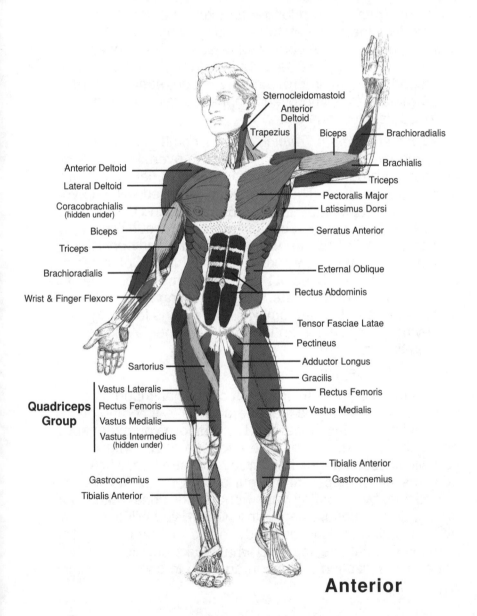

Sternocleidomastoid
Anterior Deltoid
Trapezius
Biceps
Brachioradialis
Brachialis
Triceps
Pectoralis Major
Latissimus Dorsi
Serratus Anterior
External Oblique
Rectus Abdominis
Tensor Fasciae Latae
Pectineus
Adductor Longus
Gracilis
Rectus Femoris
Vastus Medialis
Tibialis Anterior
Gastrocnemius

Anterior Deltoid
Lateral Deltoid
Coracobrachialis
(hidden under)
Biceps
Triceps
Brachioradialis
Wrist & Finger Flexors
Sartorius
Vastus Lateralis
Rectus Femoris
Vastus Medialis
Vastus Intermedius
(hidden under)
Gastrocnemius
Tibialis Anterior

Quadriceps Group

Anterior

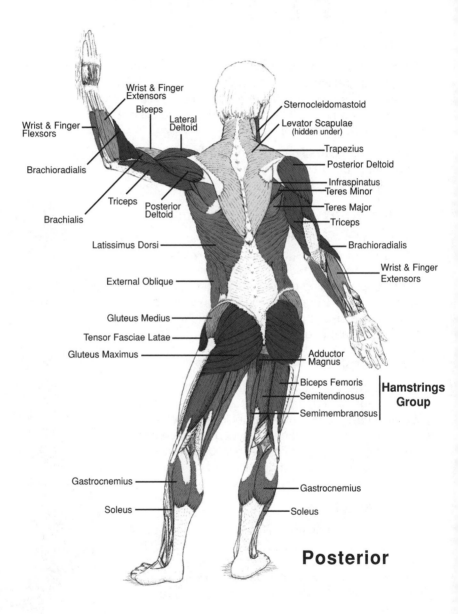

Wrist & Finger Extensors

Biceps

Wrist & Finger Flexsors

Lateral Deltoid

Brachioradialis

Triceps

Posterior Deltoid

Brachialis

Latissimus Dorsi

External Oblique

Gluteus Medius

Tensor Fasciae Latae

Gluteus Maximus

Gastrocnemius

Soleus

Sternocleidomastoid

Levator Scapulae
(hidden under)

Trapezius

Posterior Deltoid

Infraspinatus
Teres Minor

Teres Major

Triceps

Brachioradialis

Wrist & Finger Extensors

Adductor Magnus

Biceps Femoris

Semitendinosus

Semimembranosus

Hamstrings Group

Gastrocnemius

Soleus

Posterior

9

EVALUATING YOUR
PHYSIQUE

BODY TYPES

Body type is an important consideration when establishing your objectives and choosing a training method. If your desired physique opposes your natural body type, changes may take longer. That is not to say gains are impossible, only that it is more difficult to work against your genetic profile.

The standard classification of body types is based on body shape as opposed to body size. There are three types of bodies, that are best explained in the extreme.

Endomorph

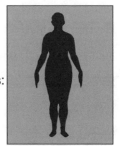

Endomorphs tend to store fat easily and are prone to heavy upper arms, legs and waist. Physical activities should be restricted to those that minimize joint stress: for example, cycling rather than jogging. A combination of weight training for definition and aerobic exercise is particularly effective in re-shaping the endomorph body.

Ectomorph

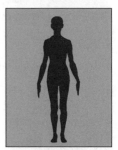

Ectomorphs are usually thin, and have a low percentage of body fat. They are extremely efficient in burning calories and often excel in endurance activities. Weight training for hypertrophy, combined with an increased caloric intake is ideal for the ectomorph who wants muscular size.

Mesomorph

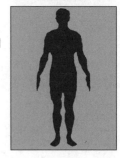

The mesomorph is naturally muscular with a powerful neck and broad shoulders. Mesomorphs excel in sports such as sprinting and field events. This body type responds very well to weight training complimenting its already muscular structure.

YOUR

MEASUREMENTS

Actual

- Measure your muscles either flexed or relaxed, but write down which so you are consistent each time you do an evaluation.
- Take your measurements in the middle of the muscle and keep a consistent tension on the tape.
- Don't measure yourself immediately after a workout. Wait 24 hours.
- Measure your bodyparts in the same place each time you do an evaluation and write the size in the ACTUAL column.

Goal

- Determine whether you want to increase or decrease the size of a particular body part and by how much. Add or subtract inches to each ACTUAL bodypart measurement to determine your ideal size and list the size under GOAL.
- Neck, Hips, Ankles (and Chest for women) normally remain the same as ACTUAL unless you are overweight.

Difference

- Subtract the GOAL amount from the ACTUAL amount and the difference is the amount you want to lose or gain.

DATE:		BODY WEIGHT:	

SIZE	ACTUAL	GOAL	DIFFERENCE
NECK	_____ -	_____ =	_____
BICEPS	_____ -	_____ =	_____
FOREARMS	_____ -	_____ =	_____
CHEST	_____ -	_____ =	_____
WAIST	_____ -	_____ =	_____
HIPS	_____ -	_____ =	_____
THIGHS	_____ -	_____ =	_____
CALVES	_____ -	_____ =	_____
ANKLES	_____ -	_____ =	_____

How To Set Up A
PROGRAM

1. ESTABLISH GOALS

Begin by setting specific and realistic goals. Ideally, set a long term goal and then set a series of short term goals toward the attainment of the long term goal. Some types of goals include ;
- Build muscle size
- Trim and tone physique
- Increase strength

If your goals involve changing your physique you can use the measurements page to design your goals very specifically. If your goals involve losing a considerable amount of fat, then a greater aerobic component is required. It is important to focus on daily goals of constant improvement and the short and long term goals will take care of themselves.

Once you have decided on your goals, list exactly how you will attain them, including the number of workouts/week, type of activity, time of day for workout, and how you will incorporate this into your weekly schedule. Look to see what changes in your lifestyle you will have to make to accommodate the new program.

Make sure your program includes the basic components of a successful program.

PROGRAM COMPONENTS

Aerobic Exercise	Nutrition
Weight Training	Stretching

2. CHOOSE A TRAINING METHOD

The training method you select should reflect both your present fitness level and your future goals. If you are a beginner start slowly, gradually increasing the frequency and intensity of your training. A realistic schedule is both safer and easier to follow. Here are some key elements you should remember when designing your personal program:

Most training methods can be used to gain muscle size, strength, or definition. A good way to decide which method is best for you, is to examine your present physique and determine your objectives. Do you want to have bulging muscles, or do you prefer a moderate but well defined body? Perhaps you are involved in a sport where rapid speed and power are required.

HYPERTROPHY
(MUSCLE DEVELOPMENT)

Hypertrophy shocks the muscles to stimulate a rapid increase in size. This is achieved by lifting moderate to heavy weight, usually 6 to 12 repetitions, and between 2 to 6 sets. Rest between sets should be kept between 1 to 1 1/2 minutes.

> **HYPERTROPHY**
> REPS 6 - 12
> SETS 2 - 6
> REST 1 - 1.5 mins

DEFINITION

This method of training stimulates a high cardiovascular rate and helps burn excess fatty tissue, while adding definition to the muscles. Exercises are commonly performed for 18 to 25 repetitions and 3 to 4 sets, using a light to moderate weight. Rest between sets should be from 30 to 60 seconds.

> **DEFINITION**
> REPS 18 - 25
> SETS 3 - 4
> REST 30 - 60 secs

STRENGTH
(NEUROLOGICAL STRENGTH)

The purpose of this method is to build neurological strength. Normally, 4 to 6 sets are performed with repetitions between 2 and 5. The weight lifted is usually very heavy, and therefore rest between sets is extended to 3 to 4 minutes.

> **STRENGTH**
> REPS 2 - 5
> SETS 4 - 6
> REST 3 - 4 mins

3. COMPONENTS OF A SUCCESSFUL STRENGTH TRAINING PROGRAM

✔ **Frequency**. Exercise each muscle group 2-4 times per week. Allow a minimum of 48 hours rest for each muscle group worked. If you are doing a total body workout, three training sessions per week, performed on every second day, is adequate.

✔ **Duration**. A weight training routine should take anywhere from 45 minutes to 1 hour to complete. Add another 20 to 60 minutes if you are including aerobics.

✔ **Range of Motion**. Moving through a complete range of motion (ROM) allows the muscle to stretch before contraction and increases the number of fibers being recruited. This produces maximum contraction and force. By working the full ROM flexibility will be maintained or even increased.

✔ **Speed of Movement**. Strength training movements should be slow and controlled. Do not use momentum to complete an exercise. Momentum puts unnecessary stress on tendons, ligaments, and joints and does not develop increased strength.

✔ **Proper Form**. Focus on the proper motion of the exercise, while concentrating on the specific muscles being used. Do not sacrifice proper form to lift heavier weight or perform more repetitions

.✔ **Change Routine**. If you want to make changes in the exercises you do, wait until about the six week point. Ideally, when you reach an evaluation page in the Training Log, review your workouts and decide at that time if you want to change any of the exercises.

✔ **Rest Interval**. Allow a brief pause between sets to give the muscles a chance to partially recover before working them again. For hypertrophy or muscle size development allow 1 to 1.5 minutes; for endurance allow 30 to 60 seconds; and for strength allow 3-4 minutes.

✔ **Breathing.** Never hold your breath during any part of an exercise. Holding your breath may cause severe intra-thoracic pressure and raise blood pressure leading to dizziness, blackout or other complications. The rule of thumb is to exhale on exertion and inhale on the return part of the exercise

4. EXERCISE ORDER

When designing a strength training routine, always try to work the larger muscle groups first. Exercises that involve more than one muscle group (compound exercises) should be at the beginning of the routine and exercises that involve only one muscle group (isolation exercises) should follow. This will prevent your muscles from becoming prematurely tired.

Order of Muscle Groups by size for;

1) Upper Body 2) Lower Body 3) Abdominal and Lower back.

Upper Body

- Chest (pectoralis major and pectoralis minor)
- Upper back (latissimus dorsi and rhomboids)
- Shoulders (anterior, medial, and posterior deltoids and trapezius)
- Rotator cuff (supraspinatus, infraspinous, teres major and minor, and subscapularis)
- Triceps(long, medium, and short heads)
- Biceps (biceps brachii, brachialis, brachioradialis)
- Forearms (flexors and extensors)

Lower Body

- Gluteal muscle group (buttocks)
- Hip muscle group (psoas, adductors, and abductors)
- Quadriceps muscle group (vastus medialis, vastus lateralis, vastus intermedius, and rectus femoris)
- Hamstrings muscle group (semimembranosus, semitendinosus, and biceps femoris)
- Calf muscle group (soleus, gastrocnemius, anterior tibialis)

Abdominals and Lower Back

- Abdominals (transverse and rectus abdominus, and obliques)
- Lower back (quadratus lumborum and erector spinae)

5. DESIGN YOUR ROUTINE

Step 1

Decide which of the training methods (from page 13) is best suited to accomplish your particular goals.

Step 2

Go through the exercise descriptions and select one or two exercises per bodypart. Don't leave any of the bodypart sections out or your routine will not be balanced. If you are trying to increase muscle size it is alright to add extra exercises to the area you want to work.

Step 3

You can either divide the exercises into upper body and lower body or keep them all together. If you only select one exercise per body part the whole routine can be done in the same workout. If you have more than 12 exercises you may want to split the routine into two or more sections. Consider each section a separate workout (see sample routines on page 24). The choice is yours.

Step 4

Order the exercises in the workout according to the type of exercise and the muscles used (see page 15).

Step 5

Write down the exercises along with the number of repetitions and the number of sets on the first page in the Training log. Don't write in the amount of weight lifted (also called workload), until you do the actual exercise. When starting a new routine start off with light weights and gradually increase the amount from set to set until you reach a weight you are comfortable with.

Step 6

Review and practice the components of a successful strength training program from page 14.

> ### REPETITIONS, SETS , AND WORKLOAD
> Repetitions, also known as "reps",are the number of times an exercise is done consecutively without rest. One complete series of continuous, consecutive repetitions is called a Set. Workload refers to the amount of weight used in working a particular muscle or muscle group.

16

WEIGHT TRAINING
SAFETY TIPS

✔ **Always warm up before you start a workout.** Try to do a total body warm-up before you start training. A good example of a total body warmup is using a rowing or skiing machine. It is especially important to warm up the specific muscle groups you are going to be using. A warm-up can be as simple as performing the specific exercise at 25% to 50% of the weight you normally lift at very high reps.

✔ **Use proper posture.** Maintaining proper posture will greatly reduce chances of injury and maximize exercise benefit. When standing always keep your feet shoulder width apart. Do not lock your knees; it puts an unnecessary strain on them. Keep your back flat and straight, making sure not to twist or arch it in order to complete an exercise.

✔ **Use proper form.** Focus on only working the muscle groups intended for the exercise you are doing. If you feel strain elsewhere you may need someone to critique your exercise motion or reevaluate the amount of weight you are lifting. Keeping proper form also means lifting in a smooth fluid motion. Know when your muscles are too tired to keep going.

✔ **Breathe properly.** Never hold your breath during any part of an exercise. Holding your breath may cause severe intra-thoracic pressure and raise blood pressure leading to dizziness, blackout or worse! The rule of thumb is to exhale slowly on exertion and inhale on the return part of the exercise.

✔ **Stop training if you feel pain.** If you feel pain during a specific exercise stop immediately. Any continuation may aggravate an existing injury. Reevaluate your routine to make sure you are doing a proper warm-up. Decrease the amount of weight you are lifting.

STRETCHING

BY NIKOS APOSTOLOPOULOS, BPHE, NCCP-L3, AACA, AAA

Frequency/Intensity/Duration

Frequency:	Try to stretch everyday; do each stretch 3 times
Intensity:	Light pressure, about 30-40% of max
Duration:	Hold each stretch between 30 to 60 seconds: <u>Not more than 90 seconds</u>

If you are unable to stretch on a daily basis a pre and post workout stretch is necessary. After a warmup, but before the workout, do each of the 13 stretches twice and after the workout one more time, for a total of three reps for each stretch.

Gastrocnemius Stretch

1

- Keep the front knee slightly bent with the back knee straight and heel down
- Lean hips forward
- Repeat with other leg

Soleus Stretch

2

- Keep both knees slightly bent
- Lean forward from hips
- Keep heels on the ground
- Repeat with other leg

Glute Stretch

3

- Place left ankle just past the right knee
- Right foot should be placed against wall so that right knee is at 90 degrees
- Make sure the pelvis/hip area is not floating in air; keep it as close to the ground as possible
- Keep shoulders on the ground
- Repeat on other side

Hamstring Stretch

- Best performed on a corner wall so that one leg is up and the other straight
- Keep the knee of the leg on the wall slightly bent (do not force straight)
- Keep hips and pelvis square
- Place a pillow under your pelvis/abdominal wall if you feel a pull in that area.
- Repeat with other leg

Groin Stretch

- Make sure both upper and lower back is flat against a wall
- Keep shoulder level and square
- Do not force groin muscles to be stretched

Piriformis Stretch

- Try to keep shoulders and pelvis/hips on ground
- Place right foot on opposite side of the left knee
- Gently pull knee toward the floor with left arm
- Repeat on other side
- If you have difficulty reaching knee place more pillows behind neck and shoulders

Outer Leg Stretch

- Try to keep shoulders and pelvis/hips on ground
- Bring left foot up to rest on the right knee
- Thigh should be at 90 degrees to upper body
- Gently pull knee toward the floor with right arm
- Repeat on other side
- If you have difficulty reaching knee place more pillows behind neck and shoulders

Hip Flexor Stretch

- Make sure both hips and pelvis are square
- Do not let front knee move beyond 90 degrees
- Try to keep lower back and upper body straight
- Repeat with other leg forward

19

Lower Back Stretch

- Keep toes ankles and knees together
- Bring knees up until they are 90 degrees with upper body
- Slowly move top shoulder back while trying to keep knees together
- Repeat on other side

Tricep/Rhomboids/ Rear Deltoids Stretch

- Make sure shoulders are square and down
- Slowly and gently pull arm across front of body
- Try to keep lower back and upper body straight

Upper Deltoid Stretch

- Grasp elbow of left arm with right hand behind the back
- Keep the shoulders down
- Do not force this stretch

Upper Trapezius/Neck/ Deltoid/Arm Stretch

- Hold onto the side of a bench or chair
- Make sure shoulders are square and down
- Keep neck upright and not hanging forward
- Gently shift or move neck away from shoulder being stretched

Chest/Anterior Deltoid Stretch

- Place hand on wall so that arm is down and slightly behind the back
- Make sure shoulders are square and down
- Place feet shoulder width apart
- Gently twist body away from arm on wall

20

WOMEN AND
WEIGHT TRAINING

One of the most common concerns for women is after starting a weight training program, they will develop large bulging muscles. The hormone associated with muscle growth is called testosterone. Steroids are a derivative of testosterone. Because women lack this particular hormone severe muscle growth is unlikely, however, women can experience increases in strength just as significant as those of men.

Weight training helps to reduce the chance of suffering from osteoporosis. This disease, which is a weakening of the bones, is experienced more often in women than men. The body responds to the stress of weight training by reinforcing the bones with calcium, vitamin D and other vitamins and minerals.

THE SECRET TO EFFECTIVE FAT LOSS

Most North Americans respond to weight gain by immediately starting a low calorie diet. Unfortunately, without exercise, a diet may be ineffective and actually increase the amount of fat your body is likely to store. About 25% of weight lost from a low calorie diet is lean muscle tissue leading to a slower metabolism. Over 90% of those who begin a low calorie diet without exercise, gain back more weight than they started with. The worst part of this process is much of the lean muscle tissue lost while dieting is replaced with fat.

The best way to deal with unwanted flab is to firstly begin an exercise program which includes both weight training for increased lean muscle tissue and aerobic activity to burn off body fat and secondly, a monitored and balanced nutritional intake.

WEIGHT TRAINING
AFTER 70

Regular resistance training has major health benefits for the elderly. Some of the benefits associated with regular exercise are decreased insomnia, better circulation, increased mobility, increased range of motion, a decrease in the risk and severity of depression and an increase in overall well being.

Strength training leads to a greater sense of independence. since many daily activities, such as carrying groceries or vacuuming are made easier. Moreover, since weight training decreases the chance of osteoporosis, the likelihood of debilitating fractures caused by falls is also reduced. A study recently published in *The New England Journal of Medicine* shows a group of subjects with a median age of 89 years could significantly increase their strength levels (as high as 110% of previous strength levels) through weight training, proving that one is never to old to build muscle.

94 year old Carolina, still believes in regular exercise

Exercise shouldn't be intimidating. Often there are knowledgeable people around, all you have to do is ask.

How To Get The Most From
THIS JOURNAL

✔ From one workout to the next strive for <u>slow</u> and <u>consistent</u> <u>increases</u> in either the amount of weight lifted, repetitions, or sets performed.

✔ Combine your weight training and aerobic sessions together; spending 30+ minutes on aerobics and one hour for weight training

✔ Workout (aerobics & weights) 3 to 4 times per week

✔ Use your entries in the training log to compare past performance to a present performance. For instance, suppose in your third workout you could bench press 80lbs. and two months later, you can bench press 120 lbs.; your strength has increased by 50%. example: (120 lbs. divided by 80 lbs. = 1.5, then you subtract 1 and multiply by 100 to get the percentage increase in strength: 50%)

✔ Study your workouts for trends. If you notice unusual increases or decreases in your performance, look at the other factors to see what might be the cause, for instance; amount of sleep, meals (type of food & timing between meals and workout), your mood before workout, time of day of workout, any other factors (flu, cold, headache, emotional stress)

✔ If you miss some workouts because of illness or vacation don't get discouraged. Start back to your regular routine as quickly as possible.

✔ If you sustain an injury or experience discomfort while performing a particular exercise make a note in your log and the next time you talk to a recognized professional ask her/him to check your form.

✔ Reviewing previous workouts will help you realize when you have reached a sticking point or barrier (plateaus may be normal).

✔ Check to see if you are gaining weight without losing size; it means you are replacing fat with muscle, since muscle is heavier than fat.

✔ Preplan your meals to ensure the proper amount of calories and percentages of nutrients.

SAMPLE
ROUTINES

BY SCOTT LIVINGSTON, B.SC., C.A.T.(C) C.S.C.S.

Hypertrophy (Muscle Size)   `Moderate Weight`

Rest period between sets: 1- 1.5 minutes

Beginner Routine
Two days on, one day off

	Sets	Reps.
Day 1		
- Bench Press	3	10-12
- Incline Press (DB)	3	10-12
- Chins	3	10-12
- Seated Pulley Row	3	10-12
- Tricep Extensions	3	10-12
- Tricep Pushdown	3	10-12
- Bicep Curls	3	10-12
- Dumbbell Curls	3	10-12
- Crunches	3	20
Day 2		
- Shoulder Press (Front)	3	10-12
- Lateral Raises	3	10-12
- Squats	3	10-12
- Leg Curls	3	10-12
- Leg Extensions	3	10-12
- Leg Press	3	10-12
- Standing Calf Raise	3	18-20
- Seated Calf Raise	3	18-20
- Back Extensions	3	20

Advanced Routine
Three days on, one day off

	Sets	Reps
Day 1		
- Bench Press	4	10-12
- Incline Press (DB)	4	10-12
- Flyes	4	10-12
- Dips	4	10-12
- Lying Tricep Press	4	10-12
- Tricep Extensions	4	10-12
- Full Sit-ups	4	20-30
- Crunches	3	20-30
Day 2		
- Chins	4	10-12
- Seated Pulley Row	4	10-12
- Lat. Pulldows	4	10-12
- Back Extensions	4	15
- Bicep Curls	4	10-12
- Preacher Curls (DB)	4	10-12
- Dumbbell Curls (Incline)	4	10-12
Day 3		
- Shoulder Press	4	10-12
- Upright Rows	4	10-12
- Lateral Raises	4	10-12
- Squats	4	10-12
- Leg Curls	4	10-12
- Leg Extensions	4	10-12
- Leg Press	4	10-12
- Standing Calf Raise	4	18-20
- Seated Calf Raise	4	18-20

Don't Forget your Aerobic Training

Definition (Muscle Toning)   **Light Weight**

Rest period between sets: 30-60 Seconds

Beginner Routine
Two days on, one day off

Day 1	Sets	Reps.
- Bench Press (DB)	3	18-20
- Flyes (Incline)	3	18-20
- Lat Pulldowns(Back)	3	18-20
- Seated Pulley Row	3	18-20
- Kickbacks	3	18-20
- Concentration Curls	3	18-20
- Side Crunches	3-4	30
- Crunches	3-4	30

Day 2	Sets	Reps.
- Arnold Press	3	18-20
- Lateral Raises	3	18-20
- Squats	3	18-20
- Leg Curls	3	18-20
- Leg Extensions	3	18-20
- Seated Calf Raise	3	22-24
- Standing Calf Raise	3	22-24

Advanced Routine
Three days on, one day off

Day 1	Sets	Reps
- Bench Press (DB)	3-4	18-20
- Flyes (Incline)	3-4	18-20
- Flyes	3-4	18-20
- Tricep Extension	3-4	18-20
- Kickbacks	3-4	18-20
- Tricep Press (DB)	3-4	18-20
- Crunches	4	40
- Side Crunches	4	40

Day 2	Sets	Reps
- Chins	3-4	18-20
- Bent Over Row (DB)	3-4	18-20
- Lat. Pulldows	3-4	18-20
- Good Mornings	3-4	18-20
- Preacher Curls (DB)	3-4	18-20
- Dumbbell Curls (Incline)	3-4	18-20
- Concentration Curls	3-4	18-20

Day 3	Sets	Reps
- Front Deltoid Raise	3-4	18-20
- Seated Lateral Raise	3-4	18-20
- Arnold Press	3-4	18-20
- Squats	3-4	18-20
- Lunges	3-4	18-20
- Leg Curls (DB)	3-4	18-20
- Leg Extensions	3-4	18-20
- Standing Calf Raise	3	22-24
- Seated Calf Raise	3	22-24

☞ **If you are a beginner, a three week pre-routine schedule is recommended. For the first week, simply perform the exercises with no weight. This will help you develop proper form. Balance is developed in the second and third weeks, as you add a few pounds to each exercise. Once the three weeks have ended, begin adding more weight. The desired objective should be to lift as much weight as possible, in a controlled movement throughout the appropriate number of repetitions.**

Strength — **Heavy Weight**

Rest period between sets: 3-4 Minutes

Beginner Routine
Two days on, one day off

	Sets	Reps.
Day 1		
- Bench Press	6	3-5
- Incline Press	6	3-5
- Bent Over Rows	6	3-5
- Deadlift	6	3-5
- Lying Tricep Press	6	3-5
- Bicep Curls (EZ Curl bar)	6	3-5
- Full Sit-ups (Rotary)	4	30
-		
Day 2		
- Shoulder Press (Back)	6	3-5
- Shoulder Shrugs	6	3-5
- Squats	6	3-5
- Leg Press	6	3-5
- Standing Calf Raise	6	3-5
- Back Extensions	4	30

Advanced Routine
Three days on, one day off

	Sets	Reps
Day 1		
- Bench Press	6	3-5
- Incline Press (DB)	6	3-5
- Flyes	6	3-5
- Close Grip Bench Press	6	3-5
- Lying Tricep Press	5	3-5
- Tricep Extensions	6	3-5
- Full Sit-ups (Rotary)	4	30
Day 2		
- Bent Over Rows	6	3-5
- Lat. Pulldows	6	3-5
- Deadlift	6	3-5
- Bicep Curls (EZ Curl bar)	6	3-5
- Preacher Curls	6	3-5
Day 3		
- Shoulder Press (Back)	6	3-5
- Shoulder Shrugs	6	3-5
- Squats	6	3-5
- Leg Press	6	3-5
- Standing Calf Raise	6	3-5

Treating Injuries

If you injure yourself during training, follow the four steps of Rest, Ice, Compression and Elevation; otherwise known as RICE.

R) Give the injured area sufficient rest before working it again.

I) Apply a cold compress to the area to reduce swelling.

C) Apply pressure to the injured area.

E) If the injured area is an extremity: hand, foot, etc. elevate the area.

TRAINING
TECHNIQUES

If you are an intermediate or advanced weight lifter, here are some techniques you may want to incorporate into your routine.

Forced Reps

Forced reps allow you to add a few extra repetitions to the set. A partner slowly helps you lift the bar past the sticking point, allowing you to extend the set past positive failure. Positive failure is achieved when the muscles are incapable of performing another repetition, while maintaining proper exercise form.

Cheating Reps

Cheating reps are another way to extend a set past positive failure. Once a set has reached positive failure, use added body motion to move past the sticking point to add a few extra repetitions. This technique is not recommended and can be dangerous if you attempt to bounce or throw the weight.

Bi & Tri Sets

These techniques are difficult to perform in a crowded gym because all the exercises must be prepared with the proper weight prior to beginning the sets. The goal of Bi and Tri sets is to perform 2-3 different exercises, one after the other, in a combined set. An example of a tri set routine for shoulders would look something like this.

TRI SET SHOULDER ROUTINE
UPRIGHT ROWS
SHOULDER PRESS
SHOULDER SHRUGS

Supersets

Supersets are normally done when time is limited and you want a quick workout. The idea behind a superset is to work two opposing muscles using different exercises. As you switch exercises, very little rest is taken, moving directly back and forth between the opposing muscles.

> **SUPERSET FOR ARMS**
> TRICEP KICKBACKS
> BICEP CURLS

Preexhaust

This technique is especially effective when working the chest, shoulders or legs. The idea is to work a major muscle with an isolation exercise (exercises that work only one muscle such as flyes, shrugs or leg extensions) before moving to a compound exercise (exercises that work several different muscles such as the bench press, shoulder press, or squats). Compound exercises often incorporate associated weaker muscles that sometimes tire prematurely. To preexhaust the chest, do a set of flyes before addressing the bench press. As a result, the triceps will not fatigue before the pectorals.

Cycle Training

This technique combines the three training methods over a set period of time. With cycle training each method is performed for approximately six weeks in the following order:

Hypertrophy >> Strength >> Definition

Cycle training provides your body with the benefits of each training method. It is especially beneficial for those wanting to maintain an already well proportioned physique.

Circuit Training

Circuit training requires going through a series of exercises, performing one set per exercise. Once the circuit is completed, you start over, performing a second, third or fourth set, depending on your routine. There are usually different circuits offered for beginners, intermediate and advanced individuals. The amount of weight lifted, the number of reps and sets can still be varied making circuit training extremely effective.

AEROBIC
TRAINING

A erobic exercise can be any type of activity that causes your heart rate to increase and makes you breathe harder than normal. By definition aerobic means "with oxygen".

Oxygen combusts with fats and carbohydrates to the create energy you need to continue the activity. As a fat burner, aerobic activity is particularly effective if you can maintain the activity for a minimum of 20 minutes. Put simply the body has two sources of energy; sugar and fat. The sugar or glycogen is stored in the muscles and is the easiest form of energy for your body to use. Fat requires more work to be used as energy and your body will resist using it unless it runs out of sugar energy.

If you are exercising at a fairly hard rate, which can be measured by taking your pulse, you should deplete the glycogen in your muscles in about 10-15 minutes. When the muscle runs out of sugar to burn it will begin metabolizing fat as energy. This is the reason that if you are trying to burn fat you must maintain the activity for a minimum of 20 minutes. The longer you can maintain the activity without stopping the more fat you can burn. If you stop or slow down your body takes the opportunity to replace its sugar energy stores.

The Formula for Calculating Target Heart Rate Range

Start by calculating your Maximal Heart Rate (MHR). By multiplying your MHR by upper and lower percentages you can calculate your Target Heart Rate (THR) range.

1) Calculate your approximate Maximal Heart Rate (MHR) by subtracting your age from 220. Example: 220-25 (age) =195 (MHR of a 25 year old)

2) Then to calculate your Target Heart Rate (THR) range, multiply the MHR by 55% and 85%.

Example: 195 x.55 = 107   195 x .85 = 168

Therefore the THR range for a 25 year old is between 107 and 168 beats per minute. (Save yourself the math and just use the chart on page 30)

Target Heart Rate Chart

Age	55%	Fat Burning Zone 60%	65%	70%	Cardio Zone 75%	80%	85%
18	111	121	131	141	152	162	172
19	111	121	131	141	151	161	171
20	110	120	130	140	150	160	170
21	109	119	129	139	149	159	169
22	109	119	129	139	149	158	168
23	108	118	128	138	148	158	167
24	108	118	127	137	147	157	167
25	107	117	127	137	146	156	166
26	107	117	126	136	146	155	165
27	106	116	125	135	145	154	164
28	106	116	125	134	144	154	163
29	105	115	124	134	143	153	162
30	105	114	124	133	143	152	162
31	104	113	123	132	142	151	161
32	103	113	122	132	141	150	160
33	103	112	122	131	140	150	159
34	102	112	121	130	140	149	158
35	102	111	120	130	139	148	157
36	101	110	120	129	138	147	156
37	101	110	119	128	137	146	156
38	100	109	118	127	137	146	155
39	100	109	118	127	136	145	154
40	99	108	117	126	135	144	153
41	98	107	116	125	134	143	152
42	98	107	116	125	134	142	151
43	97	106	115	124	133	142	150
44	97	106	114	123	132	141	150
45	96	105	114	123	131	140	149
46	96	104	113	122	131	139	148
47	95	104	112	121	130	138	147
48	95	103	112	120	129	138	146
49	94	103	111	120	128	137	145
50	94	102	111	119	128	136	145
51	93	101	110	118	127	135	144
52	92	101	109	118	126	134	143
53	92	100	109	117	125	134	142
54	91	100	108	116	125	133	141
55	91	99	107	116	124	132	140
56	90	98	107	115	123	131	139
57	90	98	106	114	122	130	139
58	89	97	105	113	122	130	138
59	89	97	105	113	121	129	137
60	88	96	104	112	120	128	136
61	87	95	103	111	119	127	135
62	87	95	103	111	119	126	134
63	86	94	102	110	118	126	133
64	86	94	101	109	117	125	133
65	85	93	101	109	116	124	132
66	85	92	100	108	116	123	131
67	84	92	99	107	115	122	130
68	84	91	99	106	114	122	129
69	83	91	98	106	113	121	128
70	83	90	98	105	113	120	128
71	82	89	97	104	112	119	127
72	81	89	96	104	111	118	126
73	81	88	96	103	110	118	125
74	80	88	95	102	110	117	124
75	80	87	94	102	109	116	123
76	79	86	94	101	108	115	122
77	79	86	93	100	107	114	122
78	78	85	92	99	107	114	121
79	78	85	92	99	106	113	120
80	77	84	91	98	105	112	119
81	76	83	90	97	104	111	118
82	76	83	90	97	104	110	117
83	75	82	89	96	103	110	116
84	75	82	88	95	102	109	116
85	74	81	88	95	101	108	115
86	74	80	87	94	101	107	114
87	73	80	86	93	100	106	113
88	73	79	86	92	99	106	112
89	72	79	85	92	98	105	111
90	72	78	85	91	98	104	111

Percentages are calculated from Maximum Heart Rate using the formula 220-age=MHR

Periodically check your heart rate, while exercising, to be certain you are within the proper range. To concentrate on fat burning, keep your heart rate closer to the 65% range. To improve cardiovascular efficiency move upward, to around the 80% range. To find your target heart rate please refer to the chart on page 31. If you are a beginner, keep your heart rate in the 55% range, gradually increasing your intensity as you become accustomed to exercise.

One minute after having completed your aerobic exercise take your Final Heart Rate (FHR). The time it takes your body to recover from aerobic exercise will decrease as you become more fit. Fill in your FHR on the Training log pages next to "Final pulse".

On each of the Training log pages you will notice a box for recording your aerobic activity. You can write in the type of activity, the intensity level, the duration or amount of time spent on aerobic exercise, and your Final Pulse. The intensity level is meant to rate how hard you pushed your body and not how fast you went or how many calories you burned. Use the Rate of Perceived Exertion chart to help rate your workout intensity.

Rate of Perceived Exertion (RPE)

Rating	Description
0	Nothing at all
1	Very light
2	Light
3	Somewhat moderate
4	Moderate
5	Somewhat hard
6	Hard
7	Somewhat intense
8	Intense
9	Almost maximal
10	Maximal

Note that you should be cautious while taking your pulse at the neck; pressure receptors in the carotid artery may slow the heart giving an artificially low reading. This method may even cause fainting in susceptible individuals therefore it is safest to take your pulse at the wrist.

AEROBIC EXERCISE
EQUIPMENT

S ome of the aerobic equipment can be quite expensive but if you're going to get something, it is worth buying a quality piece of equipment which you can hand down to your children's children. Another advantage to getting a good piece of equipment is, should you ever decide to sell, it holds its value. Avoid the trap of buying inferior equipment at a low price and the only exercise you get is carrying it to the storage room.

Remember: The best piece of exercise equipment that you can get is the one you enjoy using the most.

Exercise Bikes

An exercise bike gives a good focus on the lower body, working the muscles in the legs and buttocks. Adjust the seat height so the leg has a slight bend at the knee at the pedal's lowest position. If you find the upright bikes uncomfortable, try a recumbent or semi-recumbent bike.

Rowing Machines

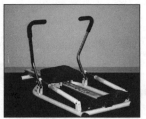

Rowing machines are great for working both the upper and lower body. The two types of rowing machines include the hydraulic shocks type and the flywheel type. Keep your back straight throughout the motion and don't lock your knees when your legs are extended.

Treadmills

Treadmills are probably the most enjoyable exercise machines and hence the most effective. Regardless of your age or fitness level, treadmills are suited for both intense and mild training.

Stairclimbers

Stairclimbers work both the legs and the buttocks. They can be an intense workout, but most have adjustable stepping speeds. Stand up straight and don't let the pedals reach either the top or bottom of the stroke.

Ski Machines

Ski machines offer a good upper and lower body workout but can be quite intense. They require a good sense of co-ordination and balance but for the right person can be a fantastic workout.

EXERCISE
DESCRIPTIONS

All exercises should result in a specific "pump" or "contraction" to the target muscle or muscle group. Locating and feeling the contraction should be the objective of each exercise. To best achieve this, follow and execute the exercises accurately. Compromising form for any reason is not recommended.

CHEST

BENCH PRESS

VARIATIONS: DUMBBELLS, CLOSE AND WIDE GRIPS, DECLINE BENCH
MUSCLES WORKED: PECTORALIS MAJOR, ANTERIOR DELTOID, TRICEPS
MACHINE EQUIVALENT: SEATED PRESS, CHEST PRESS

This exercise develops your pectoral muscles. Lie flat on the bench, with your legs comfortable, and feet either firmly on the floor or on the bench. Grip the bar slightly wider than shoulder width and slowly lower it towards the middle of your chest. Maintain control of the bar throughout the

range of motion. Avoid bouncing the bar on your chest in the lower position. Pause and then begin raising the bar slowly, until your arms are fully extended. Always keep your back flat on the bench (feet on the bench will prevent rounding of the lower back).

INCLINE PRESS

VARIATIONS: DUMBBELLS, CLOSE AND WIDE GRIPS

MUSCLES WORKED: PECTORALIS MAJOR AND MINOR, ANTERIOR AND MIDDLE DELTOID, TRICEPS

MACHINE EQUIVALENT: INCLINE PRESS, DOUBLE CHEST

This exercise is similar to the bench press, except it is performed on an incline bench. Lower the bar to your upper chest, pause, and raise. Be sure your hips stay in contact with the bench at all times and attempt to keep your elbows back.

FLYES

VARIATIONS: INCLINE BENCH, DECLINE BENCH

MUSCLES WORKED: PECTORALIS MAJOR, BICEPS, ANTERIOR DELTOID

MACHINE EQUIVALENT: PEC DEC MACHINE, VERTICAL BUTTERFLY

Lie flat on the bench holding a dumbbell in each hand. Begin with your arms straight up in front of you so that your palms face each other. Slowly lower the dumbbells to your sides in a circular fashion, bending your elbows slightly as you come down (this helps take pressure off your shoulder muscles). Once in the lowered position, hold for a

second, then raise the dumbbells in the same fashion, while squeezing your chest. (Movement resembles hugging a tree) Keep the movement smooth and concentrate on working your chest, not your arms or shoulders.

CLOSE GRIP BENCH PRESS

VARIATIONS: DUMBBELLS

MUSCLES WORKED: STERNAL AREA OF PECTORALIS MAJOR, TRICEPS, ANTERIOR DELTOID

MACHINE EQUIVALENT: CLOSE GRIPS ON CHEST PRESS

This exercise is performed on the bench press and as the name implies, is done with a close grip, (approximately 8 inches apart). Slowly lower the bar towards your lower chest, keeping your elbows in tight to your sides. Bend at the elbows, while using your triceps to push the bar

upwards. Remember not to bounce the bar in the lowered position.

TRICEPS

KICKBACK

VARIATIONS: STANDING

MUSCLES WORKED: TRICEPS; MIDDLE AND LATERAL HEADS

MACHINE EQUIVALENT: MULTI-TRICEPS, TRICEP EXTENSION

Lean over the bench, putting your left knee and left palm on the bench top. With your right hand grip the dumbbell. Your back and upper right arm should be parallel to the bench. Hold your elbow in tight to your side and straighten your elbow so that your entire arm becomes

parallel to the floor. Hold for a second then slowly return. Remember to keep your elbow fixed during the entire motion. Repeat with your left arm.

LYING TRICEP PRESS

VARIATIONS: DUMBBELLS, TRICEP BAR, EZ CURL BAR

MUSCLES WORKED: TRICEPS; MIDDLE, LATERAL AND LONG HEADS

MACHINE EQUIVALENT: TRICEP EXTENSION, MULTI-TRICEP, TRICEP PRESS

Lying on your back, hold the bar with your hands approximately eight inches apart and arms straight up. Keeping your arms parallel, while bending at the elbows, slowly lower the bar until it is just above your forehead.Come to a complete stop and and then

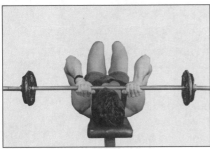

begin raising the bar back up. Your elbows should be kept in toward the chest, acting like hinges, concentrate on working the tricep muscles as you return to the start position. It is best to perform this exercise with a spotter.

☞ Keep your eating habits healthy by consciously planning your meals one day ahead. This will help ensure a proper nutritional balance and make your meals more enjoyable.

TRICEP PUSHDOWN

This exercise uses a pulley machine with a straight bar attached. Performed properly, this exercise works the entire tricep muscles. Grip the bar slightly closer than shoulder width, palms down and thumbs curled over the top of the bar with the fingers. While keeping both elbows firmly at your sides, press the bar down by straightening your arms. Pause and slowly allow the bar to return, until your forearms are at a 60 degree angle. Avoid leaning or swaying your body.

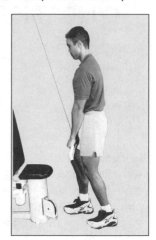

DIPS

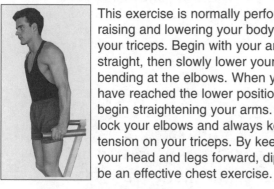

This exercise is normally performed on parallel bars raising and lowering your body using your triceps. Begin with your arms straight, then slowly lower your body bending at the elbows. When you have reached the lower position, begin straightening your arms. Do not lock your elbows and always keep tension on your triceps. By keeping your head and legs forward, dips can be an effective chest exercise.

TRICEP EXTENSION

VARIATIONS: TRICEP BAR, EZ CURL BAR

MUSCLES WORKED: TRICEPS, MIDDLE DELTOID

MACHINE EQUIVALENT: TRICEP EXTENSION, MULTI-TRICEP, TRICEP PRESS

Sit so that you straddle the bench, with a leg on either side. Hold the dumbbell overhead with both hands, palms facing upward and thumbs around the dumbbell handles. Inhale while slowly lowering the dumbbell behind your head until your forearms come in contact with your biceps. Keep your head up, back straight and hold your elbows in close to your head. Exhale and extend your elbows until your arms are straight. Make sure the motion is completely controlled.

☞   Scientific research indicates that the loss of body strength or lean muscle tissue, as a person gets older, can be reduced or delayed for decades by maintaining a strength training program.

BACK

SEATED PULLEY ROW

VARIATIONS: CLOSE AND WIDE GRIPS

MUSCLES WORKED: LATISSIMUS DORSI, MIDDLE AND LOWER TRAPEZIUS, RHOMBOIDS, BICEP

MACHINE EQUIVALENT: LEVER ROW, POWER ROW, LOW ROW

This exercise, when executed properly, works both the upper and lower back. Begin by sitting on the bench with your knees bent slightly and your upper body leaning forward. Straighten your back, keeping it set. Once your back is straight and vertical, pull the bar in toward your mid section. Slowly release and move back into the starting position. Be very careful when straightening your back: if any discomfort is felt you should discontinue the exercise and have your form checked by a professional trainer.

Warning: As with all exercises, back exercises should be performed with a light weight, slowly progressing to a heavier weight. A small miscalculation could have you in bed for a week with lower back pain, so be careful!!!

LAT PULLDOWNS

VARIATIONS: FRONT AND FRONT WITH A CLOSE GRIP

MUSCLES WORKED: LATISSIMUS DORSI, MIDDLE AND INFERIOR TRAPEZIUS, RHOMBOIDS, TERES MAJOR, SUBSCAPULARIS, BICEPS, FOREARM FLEXORS, BRACHIALIS

MACHINE EQUIVALENT: SEATED PRESS, CHEST PRESS

Setting your back in a fixed position, take a wider than shoulder width grip of the bar. Be sure your knees are tightly secured beneath the padded rests. Slowly pull the bar downward, toward your upper chest, bending your arms at the elbows. Hold for a second, then slowly allow your arms to straighten, while resisting with your back. This exercise, if done correctly, will increase your overall back width.

GOOD MORNINGS

MUSCLES WORKED: LOWER BACK

MACHINE EQUIVALENT: LOWER BACK MACHINE

Standing with your legs shoulder width apart, grip a barbell wider than shoulder width and bring it straight above your head, then carefully lower the bar behind your neck, so that it rests on the back of your shoulders. It is very important to select a weight that you can easily lift and maneuver. Bending from your hips, with your back set, slowly lower your upper body. Hold the position for a moment and then raise your upper body until you are standing erect, again. Keep your legs slightly bent to minimize any pressure on the knees. If you are a beginner, avoid heavier weight until the movement has been mastered.

DEADLIFT

VARIATIONS: BENT LEGGED DEADLIFT

MUSCLES WORKED: ERECTOR SPINAE, QUADRATUS LUMBORUM, QUADRICEPS, UPPER HAMSTRINGS

Stand upright, knees slightly bent and your feet comfortably spaced apart. With the dumbbells directly in front of you, slowly bend forward from the hips lowering the dumbbells toward the floor. Bend slightly at the knees and keep the dumbbells close to your legs as you go down and come back up. Keep your head neck and back in line and your arms straight throughout the exercise. Pause at the bottom and slowly return to the standing position, straightening your legs and hips at the same time. When performing this exercise for the first time use little or no weight as there is a possibility of lower back strain.

42

CHIN UPS

VARIATIONS: FRONT AND FRONT WITH A CLOSE GRIP, WEIGHT ASSISTED

MUSCLES WORKED: LATISSIMUS DORSI, MIDDLE AND INFERIOR TRAPEZIUS, RHOMBOIDS, TERES MAJOR, SUBSCAPULARIS, BICEPS , FOREARM FLEXORS, BRACHIALIS

MACHINE EQUIVALENT: GRAVITRON, WEIGHT ASSISTED CHIN UP

Chin ups or "Chins" as they are sometimes called, are great for developing the lats. Begin by gripping an overhead bar, slightly wider than shoulder width. Pull your body upwards, until the bar is level with your upper chest or thro at. When performing this exercise, concentrate on your lats, while keeping your elbows pointed outward. Avoid swaying the legs.

 The human body has 206 bones and over 350 muscles.

BACK EXTENSIONS

VARIATIONS: WEIGHTED

MUSCLES WORKED: ERECTOR SPINAE, QUADRATUS LUMBORUM

MACHINE EQUIVALENT: LOWER BACK MACHINE

This exercise requires a specific piece of equipment for maximum results and safety. Your ankles should be anchored under the pads, your face down and your body bent at the waist. Fold your arms at the chest and set your back in a fixed position. Begin raising

your upper body, from the waist, until it is straight. Hold the position momentarily and lower. An important point to remember when performing back extensions is not to hyper-extend the back in the raised position. This is particularity important if you are performing this exercise with weight.

BENT OVER ROW

VARIATIONS: BARBELL ROWS

MUSCLES WORKED: LATISSIMUS DORSI, MIDDLE TRAPEZIUS, POSTERIOR DELTOID, RHOMBOIDS, BICEPS

MACHINE EQUIVALENT: SEATED ROW, LOW PULLEY, VERTICAL ROW

Grip a dumbbell in your left hand. Place your right knee and right hand on the bench. Keep your left knee slightly bent and your back flat throughout the exercise. Draw the dumbbell upward toward the lower ribs, keeping your elbow close to your body on

44

the way up. Pause in the upper position for a moment, then slowly lower the dumbbell back down until your arm is fully extended. Perform a set on the left side, then switch to your right side.

BICEPS

CONCENTRATION CURL

MUSCLES WORKED: BICEPS, BRACHIALIS
MACHINE EQUIVALENT: BICEP CURL MACHINE, MULTI-BICEPS

Sit comfortably on a bench with your feet spread slightly wider than shoulder width apart. Lean over until your right elbow is placed to the inside of your right thigh, just behind your knee. Your right arm should be hanging vertical, holding the dumbbell, while your left hand is on your left knee for support. Curl your arm upward, raising the dumbbell, while holding your leg and elbow in place. The dumbbell should move toward your upper left chest Keep your head up, back straight, and avoid dropping your shoulder to lift the weight. Slowly lower and repeat. Complete the set on your right side then switch to the left.

BICEP CURL

Stand upright, knees slightly bent, and your feet comfortably spaced apart. With the dumbbells directly in front of you, palms facing away, begin to lift both weights up toward your shoulders, keeping your elbows fixed. If you are arching your back in an effort to lift the dumbbells, use a lighter weight. Once in the upper position hold for a second, then slowly lower the dumbbells back down until your arms are fully extended.

PREACHER CURL

This exercise is a lot like the barbell curl, except your arms are resting on a padded board. This reduces arm movement, helping to isolate the biceps. A few points to remember when performing the preacher curl are not to extend your arms fully, and always keep your wrists locked. Also, avoid dropping your shoulders to help lift

the weight and keep your
buttocks on the seat.

ALTERNATING DUMBBELL CURL

VARIATIONS: STANDING, INCLINE

MUSCLES WORKED: BICEPS, BRACHIALIS

MACHINE EQUIVALENT: BICEP CURL MACHINE, MULTI-BICEPS

Sit comfortably on a bench, preferably
with the back support in position. Hold the
dumbbells at your sides with your palms
facing inward. Keeping your elbow in a
fixed position, lift the dumbbell upward,
turning your palm outward as the
dumbbell
passes your
thigh. Lift and
lower one
dumbbell, then
the other. Bring
the dumbbell as
close to your
shoulder as you
can, then lower
the dumbbell
turning your
palm inward as the dumbbell passes your
thigh again. Make sure your motions are
slow and controlled; do not use momentum
to perform this exercise.

SHOULDERS

FRONT DELTOID RAISE

MUSCLES WORKED: ANTERIOR DELTOID, UPPER TRAPEZIUS
MACHINE EQUIVALENT: NONE

Stand with your feet comfortably spaced apart. Bend your knees slightly. Hold both dumbbells in front of your body so that the palms face toward you.

Keeping your arm straight, raise one of the dumbbells directly in front of you until it reaches shoulder level. Move in a slow and controlled fashion. Hold in the upper position for a moment then slowly lower the dumbbell back down. Repeat with the other arm.

☞ When you start a weight training program its a good idea to measure your waist. If you gain weight without gaining extra inches around your waist, you are putting on lean muscle tissue.

48

LATERAL RAISES

Stand with your feet comfortably spaced apart. Bend your knees slightly. Holding the dumbbells directly in front of you, begin to lift them away from your body in an upward and outward motion. Bring your arms up until they reach shoulder level. Hold this position for a moment and then slowly lower the dumbbells back down to the beginning position.

☞ A key factor in achieving muscular strength and size is the level of intensity or effort exerted during an exercise. As the level of intensity increases so does the level of discomfort; a certain amount of pain is normal. The key to avoiding injury is being able to tell muscular pain from joint or orthopedic pain.

SHOULDER PRESS

Stand with your back straight and a barbell overhead. Slowly lower the bar to your upper chest. Concentrating the effort on your deltoids, slowly push the bar back up. When in the extended position, do not lock your arms at the elbows and

keep a constant tension on the muscles involved. Keep your feet planted on the ground and your back firmly against the rest (seated). If performing this exercise standing, you may want to offset the feet to help keep your balance.

ARNOLD PRESS

This exercise can be done seated or standing. Begin by cleaning (quickly jerking the weight up and placing yourself in a position to support it), two dumbbells to the shoulders. Your palms should be towards you, with your elbows bent. In a rotary motion, press the dumbbells up straightening your arms

and ending the exercise with your palms facing forward.

SHOULDER SHRUGS

VARIATIONS: BARBELL

MUSCLES WORKED: UPPER TRAPEZIUS

MACHINE EQUIVALENT: LOW PULLEY

Stand upright, knees slightly bent, and your feet comfortably spaced apart. Bend your knees slightly. With the dumbbells directly at your sides, slowly raise your shoulders toward your ears. Keep your arms straight and do not arch your back in an effort to lift the dumbbells higher. Pause in the upper position for a moment, then slowly lower the dumbbells back down.

LEGS

SQUAT

VARIATIONS: HALF SQUAT, FOOT POSITIONING

MUSCLES WORKED: GLUTEUS GROUP, QUADRICEPS, HAMSTRINGS, ADDUCTORS, ERECTOR SPINAE, ABDOMINALS

MACHINE EQUIVALENT: DUO SQUAT

Keep your feet shoulder width apart and your toes pointed slightly outward. With the bar placed across the lower neck and shoulders, slowly bend your knees, lowering your body as if to sit. When your thighs are parallel to the ground, stop, then begin to rise, thrusting your hips forward while keeping your back in line. Try to make the motion continuous, so as not to "stick' or "bounce" at the bottom. The weight should be felt on your heels and not your toes. Keep your head up and focused; this will improve both your balance and ability to breathe. If you feel any pressure on your back, decrease the amount of weight and have your form examined by a professional. This exercise should always be done with a spotter. If discomfort is felt along the shoulders, try wrapping a towel around the bar. Padded wraps or sponges are also a possible solution.

LUNGE

VARIATIONS: DUMBBELLS

MUSCLES WORKED: GLUTEUS GROUP, ADDUCTORS, QUADRICEPS, HAMSTRINGS

MACHINE EQUIVALENT: MULTI-HIP

Stand with your feet comfortably spaced apart. Keep your back straight and your head level to the ground throughout this exercise. Step forward about 3-4 feet with your left foot, planting it firmly on the floor. Drop your hips until your back knee nearly touches the floor. Pause for a moment, then push yourself back into starting position. Repeat with the other leg. Do not bend your front knee beyond 90 degrees (beyond your toes)

☞   A key factor effecting muscle growth is the rest they receive after being exercised. Be sure your muscles are rested for at least 48 hours before working them again.

LEG PRESS

MUSCLES WORKED: GLUTEUS GROUP, QUADRICEPS, HAMSTRINGS, ADDUCTORS

MACHINE EQUIVALENT: LEG PRESS

Sit firmly in the seat, with your feet centered and roughly 12 inches apart. Remove all locks and place your hands on the grips. Slowly lower the weight until your legs are approximately six to ten inches away from your chest. Pause, then press the weight upward. Do not lock your knees when your legs are in the extended position; always keep your knees slightly bent. Supporting the weight with your knees can cause damage to knee tissues and ligaments.

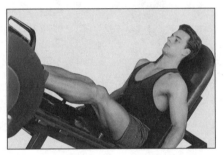

LEG EXTENSION

VARIATIONS: ONE LEGGED LEG EXTENSION

MUSCLES WORKED: QUADRICEPS GROUP

MACHINE EQUIVALENT: LEG EXTENSION MACHINE

This exercise requires a specific machine. Remember to adjust the machine to your size (seat height and back angle). With your ankles secured behind the roller pads and your arms firmly gripping the handles, extend your legs fully, hold and slowly

return. Keep the movement under control at all times and don't forget the return is as important as the actual extension.

LEG CURL

VARIATIONS: ONE LEGGED LEG CURL
MUSCLES WORKED: HAMSTRINGS, GASTROCNEMIUS
MACHINE EQUIVALENT: SEATED LEG CURL, SIDE LEG CURL

As in the leg extension, the leg curl requires a specific machine to perform the exercise. Lie face down, grip the handles and place your heels behind the roller pads. Be sure to adjust the roller pads to suit your specific size. Raise both legs, bringing them toward your buttocks, pause and straighten. Try not to lift your body off the bench while contracting your legs.

CALVES

STANDING CALF RAISE

VARIATIONS: TOES IN (WORKS LATERAL), TOES OUT (WORKS MEDIAL)
MUSCLES WORKED: GASTROCNEMIUS
MACHINE EQUIVALENT: STANDING CALF MACHINE

Stand with the padded supports on your shoulders, after adjusting the machine to suit your height. Placing the balls of your feet on the foot rest, legs slightly bent, lower and raise your body using your calf muscles. Perform the exercise slowly, making sure to descend fully before rising again. Avoid bouncing in the lower position and keep the motion smooth.

☞ When training with weights, much of the weight is transmitted to the feet. Always wear appropriate footwear to accommodate the extra weight.

SEATED CALF RAISE

VARIATIONS: DUMBBELLS

MUSCLES WORKED: SOLEUS

MACHINE EQUIVALENT: SEATED CALF MACHINE

This exercise, although similar to the Standing Calf Raise, works a different calf muscle and should not be left out of your routine. Sit with your knees under the padded rests. Your back should be straight and your toes on the foot rests. Remove all locks and slowly raise and lower the weight. When performing this exercise, avoid leaning back and always keep your hands ready to resecure the locks. As with all the exercises, keep the motion smooth and remember to breathe.

☞ Are you overtraining? Some signs include headaches, insomnia, irritability, loss of appetite, lack of energy and an elevated morning heart rate.

ABDOMINALS

CRUNCH

Similar to a sit up, the crunch involves raising your neck, shoulders and upper back off the floor in a forward arch. Begin by curling your neck and back off the floor. Keep your waist and hips on the floor, letting your abdominal muscles

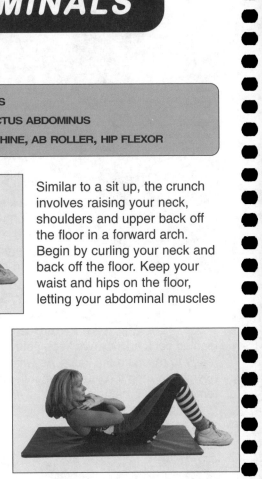

do the work. Exhale while contracting your abdominal muscles on the way up and inhale on the way down while relaxing. Reverse crunches are performed using an opposite strategy. In a rolling fashion, attempt to bring your pelvis towards your chest.

☞ Did you know that fluctuations in body weight of a few pounds is normal due to water retention.

SIT-UPS

A sit-up is performed lying down, with your feet on the floor and your knees bent. Your hands should be at the sides of your head. Begin by curling your neck and back until your elbows surpass your knees. Lower and repeat. A variation of this

exercise can be done by using a rotary motion as you raise and lower your torso. Bring your right elbow to your left knee etc.. Be sure not to pull your head upwards with your arms. When performing this exercise with weights, you will want to secure your feet. This is known as a locked sit-up.

☞ The human body contains three main types of muscles. Smooth muscles (intestinal, without conscious effort), the heart muscle, and skeletal muscles (movement muscles).

NUTRITION

The old saying you are what you eat holds a certain ring of truth to it. All the things we ingest (air, food, water) go into making our bodies function and grow. The body takes what it needs from what we give it, and then either uses those things in their raw form or transforms them into other substances that we need. This is why it is important to pay attention to what we give our bodies. A healthy diet has an appropriate combination of proteins, carbohydrates, and fats along with the proper intake of vitamins and minerals.

NUTRITION AND WEIGHT TRAINING

Diet is an important part of a successful weight training program. An active person must be aware of the types of foods he is eating and their nutritional value. By combining your weight training objectives with a balanced nutritional diet you can develop a sound overall program.

Carbohydrate, protein and fat should be consumed in specific proportional amounts. The average active person wants to take in a slightly higher than average amount of protein, to facilitate muscle repair and growth. Be careful with protein supplements and powders since the liver can only breakdown a limited quantity of protein safely. The amount of carbohydrate should also reflect the type of training you are doing. If your program involves adding definition and losing fat, you require a significant amount of calories for energy and consequently, your diet should include a greater percentage of complex carbohydrates. While fat is a necessary part of your diet it is often found in abundance within our foods. As a rule don't look to add fat to your diet, but aim at reducing your fat intake.

The ideal proportions for an active person, measured in calories is:

> • 15% PROTEIN
> • 60 -65% CARBOHYDRATE
> • 20-25% FAT

In addition, we know that the body responds better to small frequent meals. (5 instead of 3).

Protein

Blood, muscles, hair, nails, and skin are formed primarily from protein. Other than water, the human body contains more protein than anything else. It plays an important role in the reconstruction of muscle tissue. A protein deficiency could lead to impaired muscle development and yet, as with the other food elements, excess is converted to fat (stored energy) and therefore appropriate levels should be maintained.

There are 20 different amino acids used in the construction of protein. The human body can produce 11 of the amino acids, which are referred to as "non-essential", if it has sufficient carbohydrate and nitrogen levels. The other 9 "essential" amino acids, must be obtained through the foods we eat or through supplementation. Eggs, milk, meat, poultry and fish are considered complete sources of the 9 essential amino acids.

> ☞ Fat has over twice the calories, per gram, than both protein or carbohydrate. One gram of;
> Fat has **9** calories
> Protein has **4** calories
> Carbohydrate has **4** calories

Carbohydrates

Carbohydrates are the body's primary source of energy and should be the major component in our diets. Carbohydrates come in three categories:

- Monosaccharides - simple sugars (Honey and Fruits)
- Disaccharides- sucrose (Table sugar)
- Polysaccharides- complex carbohydrates (Whole grain, Pasta and Legumes)

The main difference between the three types of carbohydrates is the rate at which they are converted to blood sugar and metabolized as energy. Carbohydrates that are converted at a quick rate, such as simple sugars and sucrose, provide short term energy. Complex carbohydrates, which are converted at a slower rate, offer energy over a longer period of time. A healthy diet should consist of about 15% simple sugars and sucrose and 85% complex carbohydrates.

Fats

Fat is a concentrated source of energy. There are two types of dietary fat: saturated and unsaturated. Saturated fats harden at room temperature, where as unsaturated fats stay liquid. Put simply, it is best to avoid saturated fats. Any type of calories may be converted into body fat if we take in more than we need.

Calories

A calorie is a measure of energy. It is the amount of heat required to raise the temperature of one gram of water, one degree centigrade, at normal atmospheric pressure. A balance between the intake and expenditure of calories must exist for a person to remain at a constant weight. Any discrepancy will result in either a weight loss or gain. It is important to note that there are more than twice the amount of calories in a gram of fat than in either protein or carbohydrates. A typical gram of fat contains 9 calories whereas a single gram of protein or carbohydrate contains

> **To calculate the average calories spent per day for a moderately active person:**
>
> Multiply the persons weight in kgs. x 24 (hrs in a day) x (1 for men and .9 for women) for Basal Metabolic Rate and add 70.%.
>
> For example, a 50 kg. woman. 50 x 24 x .9 x 1.7 = 1836 calories

only 4 calories.

Vitamins

Vitamins are a necessary part of everyone's diet. Here is a list of the most important vitamins, their function, and from what foods they may be obtained. Vitamins A, D, E and K are fat soluble vitamins and may lead to toxicity if taken in excess.

Vitamin A

Function: Vitamin A helps in maintenance of the cornea, skin; bone and tooth growth

Sources: Carotene - dark green and yellow vegetables such as, carrots, beans, yams and spinach.

Retinol - liver, milk, cheese, eggs and fish liver oils.

Note: Vitamin A comes in two forms, carotene and retinol. Your body converts carotene to retinol.

Vitamin D

Function: Vitamin D assists your body, through the use of phosphorus and calcium, in maintaining strong bones and teeth.

Sources: Liver, cod liver oil, egg yolks, sunlight (your skin converts sunlight to vitamin D).

Note: Taken in excess, Vitamin D can be toxic. An excess of vitamin D can cause deposits of calcium in soft tissues such as kidneys, arteries and joints.

Vitamin E

Function: Vitamin E helps to prevent the destruction of red blood cells. It also aids in keeping a clear and well functioning cardiovascular system, thus improving blood flow.

Sources: Green vegetables, vegetable oils, raw seeds, nuts, wheat germ, whole grains and eggs.

Note: Vitamin E is considered an antioxidant and may help to decrease tissue damage caused by exercise and other sources.

Vitamin K

Function: Vitamin K helps to control the rate at which blood clots.

Sources: Brussel sprouts, cauliflower, broccoli, green leafy vegetables and tomatoes.

Vitamin C

Function: Vitamin C aids your body in the production of collagen and helps in the absorption of iron.

Sources: Citrus fruits and juices (guavas are the best known natural source), oranges, tomatoes, green peppers, cabbage, potatoes and broccoli.

Note: Vitamin C is considered an antioxidant and may help to decrease tissue damage caused by exercise and other sources.

Vitamin Bl (Thiamine)

Function: Vitamin Bl helps your body in breaking down carbohydrates to energy.

Sources: Whole grains, wheat germ, bran flakes, pork, liver and dried beans.

Note: The refinement of foods often depletes Vitamin Bl from carbohydrates.

Vitamin B2 (Riboflavin)

Function: Vitamin B2 assists your body in releasing energy from fats, carbohydrates and proteins. As well, vitamin B2 helps in the maintenance and growth of tissues.

Sources: Milk, liver, eggs, green leafy vegetables, whole grain breads and cereals, meat and legumes.

Note: Used in energy metabolization and supports normal vision and skin health.

Vitamin B3(Niacin)

Function: Used in energy metabolization and supports health of the skin, as well as the nervous and digestive system.

Sources: Poultry, tuna, fish, liver, breads and cereals, legumes.

Note: Can either be eaten or made by the body.

Vitamin B6

Function: Vitamin B6 helps in the conversion of stored liver and muscle glycogen into energy. As well, it helps your body to utilize the protein you ingest.

Sources: Fish, liver, bananas, whole grains, raw nuts, vegetables, meat and poultry.

Note: Used in amino acid and fatty acid metabolism; helps to make red blood cells.

Vitamin B12

Function: Vitamin B12 helps in the production of red blood cells.

Sources: Eggs, white fish, cheese, lean meat, liver, poultry, milk and enriched Soya milk.

Note: The liver stores a large amount of B12, making daily requirements low.

SUPPLEMENTS & ERGOGENIC AIDS

There is no such thing as a miracle solution and to be honest, nothing can replace hard work in the gym combined with a balanced diet. Supplements may be a way to acquire nutrients that may be lacking in your diet, but remember; supplements should be used in association with, and not as a substitute for the foods you eat. They are usually quite expensive and can normally be obtained through a sound diet. If you think supplementation is required in your diet, consult a licensed dietician.

Multi-vitamins/minerals

An adequate diet often contains a full compliment of

vitamins and minerals, however, taking multi-vitamins/minerals can be an effective way to ensure you are getting a full range. Be sure to choose multi-vitamins/minerals that are balanced, and as with everything else, avoid excess. Abuse of vitamins can lead to toxicity.

Amino Acids

Amino Acid supplements can come in the form of capsules, tablets, powder or liquid. Supplements which contain the full range of amino acids are best; your body can select what it needs. If you are taking amino acid supplements it is a good idea to take multi-vitamin supplements as well, since protein synthesis is co-dependent on the presence of certain vitamins. As with all supplements, begin by taking small doses and gradually work up to larger quantities if necessary. Ingesting too high a dosage of amino acids can have detrimental effects on your health and may impede or even retard muscle growth, so be careful!

Miscellaneous Powders

There are several types of bodybuilding powders on the market today. Bulk Up, Definition, Weight Gain and Carb Up are only a small sample. They can have their purpose and if chosen carefully, may help in attaining your objectives. When choosing a powder be sure to check the contents. Carbohydrates, fats and proteins should be balanced to suit your particular needs. If protein is a major concern, be sure adequate vitamins are included in the powder.

Bee Pollen (supplement)

Bee pollen is found in flowering plants or more precisely in the male seed. Amino acids, minerals and vitamins can be found in bee pollen, though their quantities are uncertain. It is a fairly expensive supplement and its benefits are unproven. It is usually found in capsule or injection form, and at present, there is no safe dosage established. Some of its speculated benefits are that it helps weight control, energizes the body and acts as an anti-aging agent.

L-Carnitine (supplement)

L-Carnitine helps promote normal growth and development. It is produced inside the body from methionine and lysine (amino acids). Natural sources of L-Carnitine can be found in dairy products, red meats, and avocados. It is also available from synthetic sources though as of yet, there is no established Recommended Dietary Allowance (RDA).

This supplement is used in the transporting of long chained fatty acids into the mitochondria where they are oxidized and thus yield energy. It has long been said that L-Carnitine aids in the building of muscle though these benefits have yet to be proven.

Ginseng (medicinal herb)

Ginseng, or rather the ginseng root is known to stimulate the brain, heart, and decrease blood sugar. It is yet to be proven that ginseng increases physical efficiency, and therefore its potential as a weight training supplement is questionable. Prices vary and there are many types available.

Inosine (nucleic acid)

Inosine is one of the nucleic acids that make-up the framework of DNA and RNA. It is the fundamental ingredient of each living cell. Inosine is found in all foods and cannot be created synthetically. Its claimed benefits are that it provides an energy boost and an extended energy duration. As a supplement the benefits of Inosine have yet to be proven.

L-Cysteine (amino acid)

L-Cysteine can be found in dairy products, eggs, meat, and some cereals. It is an essential ingredient in protein and has been claimed to build muscle, as well as bum fat, though this has not been proven.

Deficiencies of individual amino acids are unlikely, therefore supplementation is only necessary if a limited selection of foods are eaten over an extended period.

L-Lysine (amino acid)

An essential amino acid, L-Lysine helps to encourage growth and tissue repair. It also assists in the output of antibodies, hormones and enzymes. L-Lysine is available from both natural and synthetic sources. Some natural sources are cheese, eggs, fish, lima beans, milk, potatoes, red meat, soy products, and yeast. Again, single amino acid deficiencies are uncommon, therefore supplementation may prove unnecessary.

Arginine (amino acid)

Besides being an essential building block to all proteins, this amino acid has been found to stimulate human growth hormone. Arginine can be found in brown rice, chocolate, nuts, oatmeal popcorn, raisins, raw cereals, sesame and sunflower seeds, as well as whole wheat products. It has been said to build muscle and bum fat, though these findings are unproven as of yet. As with L-Lysine and L-Cysteine, deficiencies are rare and only individuals with very low protein intake should consider supplementation.

Chromium (mineral)

Chromium can be found in beef, chicken, dairy products, eggs, and whole grain products. Chromium supports glucose metabolism and aids insulin in regulating blood sugar. It also helps transfer amino acids to the heart and liver cells. A safe daily dosage for a person above the age of seven would be 0.05-0.20 mg. Supplementation may be required for anyone with insufficient caloric or dietary intake.

ANABOLIC
STEROIDS

Anabolic steroids are derivatives of testosterone, developed to increase the anabolic (growth) effects, while minimizing the androgenic (secondary male characteristics) effects.

Steroids were first used in World War II to increase the aggressiveness of the German troops. Only later in 1954 were steroids first used in athletics by the Soviets. Since then the use of steroids has literally exploded.

There are two issues concerning the use of steroids. The first involves moral, ethical and legal considerations and the second is the effect on health. Although steroids may increase the size and strength of an individual who is weight training heavily, the question remains "At What Cost?"

Some of the known side effects are:
-increased aggressiveness ('roid rage')
-accelerated atherosclerosis (leads to premature strokes and heart attacks)
-testes atrophy (shrinking of the testicles)
-infertility
-gynecomastia (breast growth)
-liver dysfunction including fatal liver cancer
-male pattern baldness
-severe acne

Women may also experience,
-increased facial and body hair
-voice changes
-clitoris hypertrophy (enlargement of the clitoris)

Some of these effects may not be reversible and can even be fatal. Due to the lack of large scale scientific studies, there are no safe types or dosages of steroids available today.

HOW TO USE THE TRAINING LOG

Heading can be used to indicate which exercise routine you are using; upper/lower body, split, circuit level etc...

Circle the arrow if you want to increase or decrease the intensity level for next workout.

Write exercises in here.

When circuit training, record your performance vertically. As you complete each circuit move to the next Set column.

Number of repetitions (reps)

Amount of weight lifted (workload)

Circle the number you percieve your intensity level to be (1 is very easy and 10 is most difficult)

Take final pulse one minute after completing exercise.

The Training Log can accomodate up to six sets.

Aerobic box

Time box

Training Log

DATE May 11   START 1:15 pm   FINISH 2:30 pm   DURATION 1h15

Aerobic Activity: Rowing Machine
Intensity level: 1 2 3 4 5 6 7 (8) 9 10   **Final pulse:** 142
Duration: 20 mins.

Increase/Decrease Intensity

		SET 1	SET 2	SET 3	SET 4	SET 5	SET 6
▲▼	Bench Press	12 @ 100	12 @ 100	12 @ 100	@	@	@
(▲)▼	Flyes	12 @ 20	12 @ 20	12 @ 20	@	@	@
▲(▼)	Pec Dec	6 @ 70	5 @ 70	6 @ 70	@	@	@
▲▼	Kickbacks	12 @ 12	12 @ 12	12 @ 12	@	@	@
▲▼	Alt. Bicep Curl	12 @ 25	12 @ 25	12 @ 25	@	@	@
▲▼	Shoulder Press	11 @ 80	10 @ 80	11 @ 80	@	@	@
▲(▼)	Upright Rows	12 @ 25	12 @ 25	12 @ 25	@	@	@
▲▼	Bent Over Row	12 @ 35	12 @ 35	12 @ 35	@	@	@
▲▼	Crunches	12 @ BW	12 @ BW	12 @ 35	@	@	@
▲▼		@	@	@			

Day 1

Training Log

DATE	START	FINISH	DURATION

Aerobic Activity:

Intensity level: 1 2 3 4 5 6 7 8 9 10

Duration: **Final pulse:**

	SET 1	SET 2	SET 3	SET 4	SET 5	SET 6
	@	@	@	@	@	@
	@	@	@	@	@	@
	@	@	@	@	@	@
	@	@	@	@	@	@
	@	@	@	@	@	@
	@	@	@	@	@	@
	@	@	@	@	@	@
	@	@	@	@	@	@
	@	@	@	@	@	@
	@	@	@	@	@	@
	@	@	@	@	@	@

Increase/Decrease Intensity

Training Log

DATE	START	FINISH	DURATION

Aerobic Activity:

Intensity level: 1 2 3 4 5 6 7 8 9 10

Duration: **Final pulse:**

	SET 1	SET 2	SET 3	SET 4	SET 5	SET 6
	@	@	@	@	@	@
	@	@	@	@	@	@
	@	@	@	@	@	@
	@	@	@	@	@	@
	@	@	@	@	@	@
	@	@	@	@	@	@
	@	@	@	@	@	@
	@	@	@	@	@	@
	@	@	@	@	@	@
	@	@	@	@	@	@

Increase/Decrease Intensity

Aerobic Activity:

Intensity level: 1 2 3 4 5 6 7 8 9 10

Duration: **Final pulse:**

DATE	START	FINISH	DURATION

SET 1   **SET 2**   **SET 3**   **SET 4**   **SET 5**   **SET 6**

Increase/Decrease Intensity

Training Log

DATE	START	FINISH	DURATION

Aerobic Activity:

Intensity level: 1 2 3 4 5 6 7 8 9 10

Duration: **Final pulse:**

Increase/Decrease Intensity

SET 1	SET 2	SET 3	SET 4	SET 5	SET 6
@	@	@	@	@	@
@	@	@	@	@	@
@	@	@	@	@	@
@	@	@	@	@	@
@	@	@	@	@	@
@	@	@	@	@	@
@	@	@	@	@	@
@	@	@	@	@	@
@	@	@	@	@	@
@	@	@	@	@	@
@	@	@	@	@	@

Aerobic Activity:

Intensity level: 1 2 3 4 5 6 7 8 9 10

Duration: *Final pulse:*

DATE	START	FINISH	DURATION

Increase/Decrease Intensity

SET 1	SET 2	SET 3	SET 4	SET 5	SET 6
@	@	@	@	@	@
@	@	@	@	@	@
@	@	@	@	@	@
@	@	@	@	@	@
@	@	@	@	@	@
@	@	@	@	@	@
@	@	@	@	@	@
@	@	@	@	@	@
@	@	@	@	@	@
@	@	@	@	@	@

Training Log

DATE	START	FINISH	DURATION

Aerobic Activity:

Intensity level: 1 2 3 4 5 6 7 8 9 10

Duration: **Final pulse:**

Increase/Decrease Intensity

SET 1	SET 2	SET 3	SET 4	SET 5	SET 6
@	@	@	@	@	@
@	@	@	@	@	@
@	@	@	@	@	@
@	@	@	@	@	@
@	@	@	@	@	@
@	@	@	@	@	@
@	@	@	@	@	@
@	@	@	@	@	@
@	@	@	@	@	@
@	@	@	@	@	@

Aerobic Activity:

Intensity level: 1 2 3 4 5 6 7 8 9 10

Duration: *Final pulse:*

DATE	START	FINISH	DURATION

SET 1	SET 2	SET 3	SET 4	SET 5	SET 6

Increase/Decrease Intensity

Training Log

DATE	START	FINISH	DURATION

Aerobic Activity:

Intensity level: 1 2 3 4 5 6 7 8 9 10

Duration: **Final pulse:**

Increase/Decrease Intensity

SET 1	SET 2	SET 3	SET 4	SET 5	SET 6
@	@	@	@	@	@
@	@	@	@	@	@
@	@	@	@	@	@
@	@	@	@	@	@
@	@	@	@	@	@
@	@	@	@	@	@
@	@	@	@	@	@
@	@	@	@	@	@
@	@	@	@	@	@
@	@	@	@	@	@

Aerobic Activity:

Intensity level: 1 2 3 4 5 6 7 8 9 10

Duration: *Final pulse:*

DATE	START	FINISH	DURATION

SET 1	SET 2	SET 3	SET 4	SET 5	SET 6

Increase/Decrease Intensity

Training Log

DATE	START	FINISH	DURATION

Aerobic Activity:

Intensity level: 1 2 3 4 5 6 7 8 9 10

Duration: _____ **Final pulse:** _____

Increase/Decrease Intensity

	SET 1	SET 2	SET 3	SET 4	SET 5	SET 6
↕	@	@	@	@	@	@
↕	@	@	@	@	@	@
↕	@	@	@	@	@	@
↕	@	@	@	@	@	@
↕	@	@	@	@	@	@
↕	@	@	@	@	@	@
↕	@	@	@	@	@	@
↕	@	@	@	@	@	@
↕	@	@	@	@	@	@
↕	@	@	@	@	@	@

Aerobic Activity:

Intensity level: 1 2 3 4 5 6 7 8 9 10

Duration: *Final pulse:*

DATE	START	FINISH	DURATION

Increase/Decrease Intensity

SET 1	SET 2	SET 3	SET 4	SET 5	SET 6
@	@	@	@	@	@
@	@	@	@	@	@
@	@	@	@	@	@
@	@	@	@	@	@
@	@	@	@	@	@
@	@	@	@	@	@
@	@	@	@	@	@
@	@	@	@	@	@
@	@	@	@	@	@
@	@	@	@	@	@

Training Log

DATE	START	FINISH	DURATION

Aerobic Activity:

Intensity level: 1 2 3 4 5 6 7 8 9 10

Duration: **Final pulse:**

Increase/Decrease Intensity

SET 1	SET 2	SET 3	SET 4	SET 5	SET 6
@	@	@	@	@	@
@	@	@	@	@	@
@	@	@	@	@	@
@	@	@	@	@	@
@	@	@	@	@	@
@	@	@	@	@	@
@	@	@	@	@	@
@	@	@	@	@	@
@	@	@	@	@	@
@	@	@	@	@	@

Aerobic Activity:

Intensity level: 1 2 3 4 5 6 7 8 9 10

Duration: _____ **Final pulse:** _____

DATE	START	FINISH	DURATION

Increase/Decrease Intensity

SET 1 @ SET 2 @ SET 3 @ SET 4 @ SET 5 @ SET 6 @

Training Log

DATE	START	FINISH	DURATION

Aerobic Activity:

Intensity level: 1 2 3 4 5 6 7 8 9 10

Duration: Final pulse:

Increase/Decrease Intensity

SET 1	SET 2	SET 3	SET 4	SET 5	SET 6
@	@	@	@	@	@
@	@	@	@	@	@
@	@	@	@	@	@
@	@	@	@	@	@
@	@	@	@	@	@
@	@	@	@	@	@
@	@	@	@	@	@
@	@	@	@	@	@
@	@	@	@	@	@
@	@	@	@	@	@

Aerobic Activity:

Intensity level: 1   2   3   4   5   6   7   8   9   10

Duration: **Final pulse:**

DATE	START	FINISH	DURATION

Increase/Decrease Intensity

SET 1	SET 2	SET 3	SET 4	SET 5	SET 6
@	@	@	@	@	@
@	@	@	@	@	@
@	@	@	@	@	@
@	@	@	@	@	@
@	@	@	@	@	@
@	@	@	@	@	@
@	@	@	@	@	@
@	@	@	@	@	@
@	@	@	@	@	@
@	@	@	@	@	@
@	@	@	@	@	@

Training Log

DATE	START	FINISH	DURATION

	SET 1	SET 2	SET 3	SET 4	SET 5	SET 6
Increase/Decrease Intensity	@	@	@	@	@	@
	@	@	@	@	@	@
	@	@	@	@	@	@
	@	@	@	@	@	@
	@	@	@	@	@	@
	@	@	@	@	@	@
	@	@	@	@	@	@
	@	@	@	@	@	@
	@	@	@	@	@	@
	@	@	@	@	@	@
	@	@	@	@	@	@

Aerobic Activity:

Intensity level: 1 2 3 4 5 6 7 8 9 10

Duration: **Final pulse:**

DATE	START	FINISH	DURATION

Increase/Decrease Intensity	SET 1	SET 2	SET 3	SET 4	SET 5	SET 6
↑↓	@	@	@	@	@	@
↑↓	@	@	@	@	@	@
↑↓	@	@	@	@	@	@
↑↓	@	@	@	@	@	@
↑↓	@	@	@	@	@	@
↑↓	@	@	@	@	@	@
↑↓	@	@	@	@	@	@
↑↓	@	@	@	@	@	@
↑↓	@	@	@	@	@	@
↑↓	@	@	@	@	@	@
↑↓	@	@	@	@	@	@

Training Log

DATE	START	FINISH	DURATION

Increase/Decrease Intensity

SET 1	SET 2	SET 3	SET 4	SET 5	SET 6
@	@	@	@	@	@
@	@	@	@	@	@
@	@	@	@	@	@
@	@	@	@	@	@
@	@	@	@	@	@
@	@	@	@	@	@
@	@	@	@	@	@
@	@	@	@	@	@
@	@	@	@	@	@
@	@	@	@	@	@

Aerobic Activity:

Intensity level: 1 2 3 4 5 6 7 8 9 10

Duration: **Final pulse:**

DATE	START	FINISH	DURATION

Increase/Decrease Intensity

SET 1	SET 2	SET 3	SET 4	SET 5	SET 6
@	@	@	@	@	@
@	@	@	@	@	@
@	@	@	@	@	@
@	@	@	@	@	@
@	@	@	@	@	@
@	@	@	@	@	@
@	@	@	@	@	@
@	@	@	@	@	@
@	@	@	@	@	@
@	@	@	@	@	@
@	@	@	@	@	@

Training Log

DATE	START	FINISH	DURATION

Aerobic Activity:

Intensity level: 1 2 3 4 5 6 7 8 9 10

Duration: **Final pulse:**

Increase/Decrease Intensity

SET 1　SET 2　SET 3　SET 4　SET 5　SET 6

@ @ @ @ @ @

@ @ @ @ @ @

@ @ @ @ @ @

@ @ @ @ @ @

@ @ @ @ @ @

@ @ @ @ @ @

@ @ @ @ @ @

@ @ @ @ @ @

@ @ @ @ @ @

@ @ @ @ @ @

@ @ @ @ @ @

Aerobic Activity:

Intensity level: *1 2 3 4 5 6 7 8 9 10*

Duration: **Final pulse:**

DATE	START	FINISH	DURATION

Increase/Decrease Intensity

SET 1   SET 2   SET 3   SET 4   SET 5   SET 6

Training Log

DATE	START	FINISH	DURATION

Aerobic Activity:

Intensity level: 1 2 3 4 5 6 7 8 9 10

Duration: **Final pulse:**

	SET 1	SET 2	SET 3	SET 4	SET 5	SET 6

Increase/Decrease Intensity

Aerobic Activity:

Intensity level: 1 2 3 4 5 6 7 8 9 10

Duration: **Final pulse:**

DATE	START	FINISH	DURATION

Increase/Decrease Intensity

SET 1	SET 2	SET 3	SET 4	SET 5	SET 6
@	@	@	@	@	@
@	@	@	@	@	@
@	@	@	@	@	@
@	@	@	@	@	@
@	@	@	@	@	@
@	@	@	@	@	@
@	@	@	@	@	@
@	@	@	@	@	@
@	@	@	@	@	@
@	@	@	@	@	@
@	@	@	@	@	@

Training Log

DATE	START	FINISH	DURATION

Aerobic Activity:

Intensity level: 1 2 3 4 5 6 7 8 9 10

Duration: **Final pulse:**

Increase/Decrease Intensity

SET 1	SET 2	SET 3	SET 4	SET 5	SET 6
@	@	@	@	@	@
@	@	@	@	@	@
@	@	@	@	@	@
@	@	@	@	@	@
@	@	@	@	@	@
@	@	@	@	@	@
@	@	@	@	@	@
@	@	@	@	@	@
@	@	@	@	@	@
@	@	@	@	@	@
@	@	@	@	@	@

Aerobic Activity:

Intensity level: 1 2 3 4 5 6 7 8 9 10

Duration: **Final pulse:**

DATE	START	FINISH	DURATION

Increase/Decrease Intensity

SET 1   SET 2   SET 3   SET 4   SET 5   SET 6

Training Log

DATE	START	FINISH	DURATION

Aerobic Activity:

Intensity level: 1 2 3 4 5 6 7 8 9 10

Duration: **Final pulse:**

SET 1	SET 2	SET 3	SET 4	SET 5	SET 6

Increase/Decrease Intensity

Aerobic Activity:

Intensity level: *1 2 3 4 5 6 7 8 9 10*

Duration: **Final pulse:**

DATE	START	FINISH	DURATION

Increase/Decrease Intensity		SET 1	SET 2	SET 3	SET 4	SET 5	SET 6
↗ ↙		@	@	@	@	@	@
↗ ↙		@	@	@	@	@	@
↗ ↙		@	@	@	@	@	@
↗ ↙		@	@	@	@	@	@
↗ ↙		@	@	@	@	@	@
↗ ↙		@	@	@	@	@	@
↗ ↙		@	@	@	@	@	@
↗ ↙		@	@	@	@	@	@
↗ ↙		@	@	@	@	@	@
↗ ↙		@	@	@	@	@	@
↗ ↙		@	@	@	@	@	@

Training Log

DATE	START	FINISH	DURATION

Increase/Decrease
Intensity

Aerobic Activity:

Intensity level: 1 2 3 4 5 6 7 8 9 10

Duration: **Final pulse:**

SET 1   SET 2   SET 3   SET 4   SET 5   SET 6

@ @ @ @ @ @
@ @ @ @ @ @
@ @ @ @ @ @
@ @ @ @ @ @
@ @ @ @ @ @
@ @ @ @ @ @
@ @ @ @ @ @
@ @ @ @ @ @
@ @ @ @ @ @
@ @ @ @ @ @

Aerobic Activity:

Intensity level: 1 2 3 4 5 6 7 8 9 10

Duration: **Final pulse:**

DATE	START	FINISH	DURATION

SET 1	SET 2	SET 3	SET 4	SET 5	SET 6

Increase/Decrease Intensity

Training Log

DATE	START	FINISH	DURATION

Aerobic Activity:

Intensity level: 1 2 3 4 5 6 7 8 9 10

Duration: **Final pulse:**

	SET 1	SET 2	SET 3	SET 4	SET 5	SET 6

Increase/Decrease Intensity

EVALUATION
PAGE

DATE: BODY WEIGHT:

STRENGTH

Exercises	Last workout	First w/o	Gain
#1	_____ -	_____ =	_____
#2	_____ -	_____ =	_____
#3	_____ -	_____ =	_____
#4	_____ -	_____ =	_____
#5	_____ -	_____ =	_____
#6	_____ -	_____ =	_____
#7	_____ -	_____ =	_____
#8	_____ -	_____ =	_____

SIZE

	Actual	Goal	Difference
Neck	_____ -	_____ =	_____
Biceps	_____ -	_____ =	_____
Forearms	_____ -	_____ =	_____
Chest	_____ -	_____ =	_____
Waist	_____ -	_____ =	_____
Hips	_____ -	_____ =	_____
Thighs	_____ -	_____ =	_____
Calves	_____ -	_____ =	_____
Ankles	_____ -	_____ =	_____

Training Log

DATE	START	FINISH	DURATION

Aerobic Activity:

Intensity level: 1 2 3 4 5 6 7 8 9 10

Duration: **Final pulse:**

Increase/Decrease Intensity

	SET 1	SET 2	SET 3	SET 4	SET 5	SET 6
	@	@	@	@	@	@
	@	@	@	@	@	@
	@	@	@	@	@	@
	@	@	@	@	@	@
	@	@	@	@	@	@
	@	@	@	@	@	@
	@	@	@	@	@	@
	@	@	@	@	@	@
	@	@	@	@	@	@
	@	@	@	@	@	@

Aerobic Activity:

Intensity level: 1 2 3 4 5 6 7 8 9 10

Duration: _____ **Final pulse:** _____

DATE	START	FINISH	DURATION

SET 1	SET 2	SET 3	SET 4	SET 5	SET 6

Increase/Decrease Intensity

Training Log

DATE	START	FINISH	DURATION

Aerobic Activity:

Intensity level: 1 2 3 4 5 6 7 8 9 10

Duration:

Final pulse:

SET 1   SET 2   SET 3   SET 4   SET 5   SET 6

Increase/Decrease Intensity

Aerobic Activity:

Intensity level: *1 2 3 4 5 6 7 8 9 10*

Duration: **Final pulse:**

DATE	START	FINISH	DURATION

SET 1 SET 2 SET 3 SET 4 SET 5 SET 6

@ @ @ @ @ @ @ @ @ @ @

Increase/Decrease Intensity

Training Log

DATE	START	FINISH	DURATION

Aerobic Activity:

Intensity level: 1 2 3 4 5 6 7 8 9 10

Duration: **Final pulse:**

Increase/Decrease Intensity

	SET 1	SET 2	SET 3	SET 4	SET 5	SET 6
	@	@	@	@	@	@
	@	@	@	@	@	@
	@	@	@	@	@	@
	@	@	@	@	@	@
	@	@	@	@	@	@
	@	@	@	@	@	@
	@	@	@	@	@	@
	@	@	@	@	@	@
	@	@	@	@	@	@
	@	@	@	@	@	@

Aerobic Activity:

Intensity level: **1 2 3 4 5 6 7 8 9 10**

Duration: _____ *Final pulse:* _____

DATE	START	FINISH	DURATION

Increase/Decrease Intensity

	SET 1	SET 2	SET 3	SET 4	SET 5	SET 6
	@	@	@	@	@	@
	@	@	@	@	@	@
	@	@	@	@	@	@
	@	@	@	@	@	@
	@	@	@	@	@	@
	@	@	@	@	@	@
	@	@	@	@	@	@
	@	@	@	@	@	@
	@	@	@	@	@	@
	@	@	@	@	@	@
	@	@	@	@	@	@

Training Log

DATE	START	FINISH	DURATION

Aerobic Activity:

Intensity level: 1 2 3 4 5 6 7 8 9 10

Duration: **Final pulse:**

	SET 1	SET 2	SET 3	SET 4	SET 5	SET 6
Increase/Decrease Intensity	@	@	@	@	@	@
	@	@	@	@	@	@
	@	@	@	@	@	@
	@	@	@	@	@	@
	@	@	@	@	@	@
	@	@	@	@	@	@
	@	@	@	@	@	@
	@	@	@	@	@	@
	@	@	@	@	@	@
	@	@	@	@	@	@
	@	@	@	@	@	@

Aerobic Activity:

Intensity level: 1 2 3 4 5 6 7 8 9 10

Duration: **Final pulse:**

DATE	START	FINISH	DURATION

	SET 1	SET 2	SET 3	SET 4	SET 5	SET 6

Increase/Decrease Intensity

Training Log

DATE	START	FINISH	DURATION

Aerobic Activity:

Intensity level: 1 2 3 4 5 6 7 8 9 10

Duration: **Final pulse:**

SET 1 SET 2 SET 3 SET 4 SET 5 SET 6

Increase/Decrease Intensity

Aerobic Activity:

Intensity level: 1 2 3 4 5 6 7 8 9 10

Duration: *Final pulse:*

DATE	START	FINISH	DURATION

SET 1	SET 2	SET 3	SET 4	SET 5	SET 6

Increase/Decrease Intensity

Training Log

DATE	START	FINISH	DURATION

Aerobic Activity:

Intensity level: 1 2 3 4 5 6 7 8 9 10

Duration: _____ **Final pulse:** _____

	SET 1	SET 2	SET 3	SET 4	SET 5	SET 6
	_ @ _	_ @ _	_ @ _	_ @ _	_ @ _	_ @ _
	_ @ _	_ @ _	_ @ _	_ @ _	_ @ _	_ @ _
	_ @ _	_ @ _	_ @ _	_ @ _	_ @ _	_ @ _
	_ @ _	_ @ _	_ @ _	_ @ _	_ @ _	_ @ _
	_ @ _	_ @ _	_ @ _	_ @ _	_ @ _	_ @ _
	_ @ _	_ @ _	_ @ _	_ @ _	_ @ _	_ @ _
	_ @ _	_ @ _	_ @ _	_ @ _	_ @ _	_ @ _
	_ @ _	_ @ _	_ @ _	_ @ _	_ @ _	_ @ _
	_ @ _	_ @ _	_ @ _	_ @ _	_ @ _	_ @ _
	_ @ _	_ @ _	_ @ _	_ @ _	_ @ _	_ @ _
	_ @ _	_ @ _	_ @ _	_ @ _	_ @ _	_ @ _

Increase/Decrease Intensity

Aerobic Activity:

Intensity level: 1 2 3 4 5 6 7 8 9 10

Duration: **Final pulse:**

DATE	START	FINISH	DURATION

Increase/Decrease Intensity

	SET 1	SET 2	SET 3	SET 4	SET 5	SET 6
	@	@	@	@	@	@
	@	@	@	@	@	@
	@	@	@	@	@	@
	@	@	@	@	@	@
	@	@	@	@	@	@
	@	@	@	@	@	@
	@	@	@	@	@	@
	@	@	@	@	@	@
	@	@	@	@	@	@
	@	@	@	@	@	@
	@	@	@	@	@	@

Training Log

DATE	START	FINISH	DURATION

Aerobic Activity:

Intensity level: 1 2 3 4 5 6 7 8 9 10

Duration: **Final pulse:**

	SET 1	SET 2	SET 3	SET 4	SET 5	SET 6

Increase/Decrease Intensity

Aerobic Activity:

Intensity level: 1 2 3 4 5 6 7 8 9 10

Duration: _____ **Final pulse:** _____

DATE	START	FINISH	DURATION

Increase/Decrease Intensity

SET 1	SET 2	SET 3	SET 4	SET 5	SET 6
@	@	@	@	@	@
@	@	@	@	@	@
@	@	@	@	@	@
@	@	@	@	@	@
@	@	@	@	@	@
@	@	@	@	@	@
@	@	@	@	@	@
@	@	@	@	@	@
@	@	@	@	@	@
@	@	@	@	@	@

Training Log

DATE	START	FINISH	DURATION

Aerobic Activity:

Intensity level: 1 2 3 4 5 6 7 8 9 10

Duration: **Final pulse:**

	SET 1	SET 2	SET 3	SET 4	SET 5	SET 6
	___@___	___@___	___@___	___@___	___@___	___@___
	___@___	___@___	___@___	___@___	___@___	___@___
	___@___	___@___	___@___	___@___	___@___	___@___
	___@___	___@___	___@___	___@___	___@___	___@___
	___@___	___@___	___@___	___@___	___@___	___@___
	___@___	___@___	___@___	___@___	___@___	___@___
	___@___	___@___	___@___	___@___	___@___	___@___
	___@___	___@___	___@___	___@___	___@___	___@___
	___@___	___@___	___@___	___@___	___@___	___@___
	___@___	___@___	___@___	___@___	___@___	___@___

Increase/Decrease Intensity

Aerobic Activity:

Intensity level: 1 2 3 4 5 6 7 8 9 10

Duration: *Final pulse:*

DATE	START	FINISH	DURATION

SET 1 SET 2 SET 3 SET 4 SET 5 SET 6

Increase/Decrease Intensity

@

Training Log

DATE	START	FINISH	DURATION

Aerobic Activity:

Intensity level: 1 2 3 4 5 6 7 8 9 10

Duration: **Final pulse:**

	SET 1	SET 2	SET 3	SET 4	SET 5	SET 6

Increase/Decrease Intensity

Aerobic Activity:

Intensity level: 1 2 3 4 5 6 7 8 9 10

Final pulse:

Duration:

DATE	START	FINISH	DURATION

Increase/Decrease Intensity

	SET 1	SET 2	SET 3	SET 4	SET 5	SET 6
	@	@	@	@	@	@
	@	@	@	@	@	@
	@	@	@	@	@	@
	@	@	@	@	@	@
	@	@	@	@	@	@
	@	@	@	@	@	@
	@	@	@	@	@	@
	@	@	@	@	@	@
	@	@	@	@	@	@
	@	@	@	@	@	@
	@	@	@	@	@	@

Training Log

DATE	START	FINISH	DURATION

Aerobic Activity:

Intensity level: 1 2 3 4 5 6 7 8 9 10

Duration: _____ **Final pulse:** _____

	SET 1	SET 2	SET 3	SET 4	SET 5	SET 6

Increase/Decrease Intensity

@ @ @ @ @ @

@ @ @ @ @ @

@ @ @ @ @ @

@ @ @ @ @ @

@ @ @ @ @ @

@ @ @ @ @ @

@ @ @ @ @ @

@ @ @ @ @ @

@ @ @ @ @ @

@ @ @ @ @ @

@ @ @ @ @ @

DATE	START	FINISH	DURATION

Aerobic Activity:

Intensity level: 1 2 3 4 5 6 7 8 9 10

Duration: **Final pulse:**

	SET 1	SET 2	SET 3	SET 4	SET 5	SET 6

Increase/Decrease
Intensity

121

Training Log

DATE	START	FINISH	DURATION

Aerobic Activity:

Intensity level: 1 2 3 4 5 6 7 8 9 10

Duration: **Final pulse:**

Increase/Decrease Intensity

SET 1	SET 2	SET 3	SET 4	SET 5	SET 6
@	@	@	@	@	@
@	@	@	@	@	@
@	@	@	@	@	@
@	@	@	@	@	@
@	@	@	@	@	@
@	@	@	@	@	@
@	@	@	@	@	@
@	@	@	@	@	@
@	@	@	@	@	@
@	@	@	@	@	@

Aerobic Activity:

Intensity level: 1 2 3 4 5 6 7 8 9 10

Duration: **Final pulse:**

DATE	START	FINISH	DURATION

	SET 1	SET 2	SET 3	SET 4	SET 5	SET 6

Increase/Decrease Intensity

Training Log

DATE	START	FINISH	DURATION

Aerobic Activity:

Intensity level: 1 2 3 4 5 6 7 8 9 10

Duration: **Final pulse:**

	SET 1	SET 2	SET 3	SET 4	SET 5	SET 6

Increase/Decrease Intensity

Aerobic Activity:

Intensity level: 1 2 3 4 5 6 7 8 9 10

Duration: *Final pulse:*

DATE	START	FINISH	DURATION

	SET 1	SET 2	SET 3	SET 4	SET 5	SET 6

Increase/Decrease Intensity

Training Log

DATE	START	FINISH	DURATION

Aerobic Activity:

Intensity level: 1 2 3 4 5 6 7 8 9 10

Duration: **Final pulse:**

SET 1	SET 2	SET 3	SET 4	SET 5	SET 6

Increase/Decrease Intensity

Aerobic Activity:

Intensity level: 1 2 3 4 5 6 7 8 9 10

Duration: **Final pulse:**

DATE	START	FINISH	DURATION

SET 1	SET 2	SET 3	SET 4	SET 5	SET 6
@	@	@	@	@	@
@	@	@	@	@	@
@	@	@	@	@	@
@	@	@	@	@	@
@	@	@	@	@	@
@	@	@	@	@	@
@	@	@	@	@	@
@	@	@	@	@	@
@	@	@	@	@	@
@	@	@	@	@	@
@	@	@	@	@	@

Increase/Decrease Intensity

Training Log

DATE	START	FINISH	DURATION

Aerobic Activity:

Intensity level: 1 2 3 4 5 6 7 8 9 10

Duration: _____ **Final pulse:** _____

Increase/Decrease Intensity

SET 1	SET 2	SET 3	SET 4	SET 5	SET 6
@	@	@	@	@	@
@	@	@	@	@	@
@	@	@	@	@	@
@	@	@	@	@	@
@	@	@	@	@	@
@	@	@	@	@	@
@	@	@	@	@	@
@	@	@	@	@	@
@	@	@	@	@	@
@	@	@	@	@	@
@	@	@	@	@	@

Aerobic Activity:

Intensity level: 1 2 3 4 5 6 7 8 9 10

Duration: Final pulse:

DATE	START	FINISH	DURATION

SET 1	SET 2	SET 3	SET 4	SET 5	SET 6
@	@	@	@	@	@
@	@	@	@	@	@
@	@	@	@	@	@
@	@	@	@	@	@
@	@	@	@	@	@
@	@	@	@	@	@
@	@	@	@	@	@
@	@	@	@	@	@
@	@	@	@	@	@
@	@	@	@	@	@
@	@	@	@	@	@

Increase/Decrease Intensity

EVALUATION
PAGE

DATE: _____ **BODY WEIGHT:** _____

STRENGTH

Exercises	LAST WORKOUT	FIRST W/O	GAIN
#1	_____ -	_____ =	_____
#2	_____ -	_____ =	_____
#3	_____ -	_____ =	_____
#4	_____ -	_____ =	_____
#5	_____ -	_____ =	_____
#6	_____ -	_____ =	_____
#7	_____ -	_____ =	_____
#8	_____ -	_____ =	_____

SIZE	ACTUAL	GOAL	DIFFERENCE
NECK	_____ -	_____ =	_____
BICEPS	_____ -	_____ =	_____
FOREARMS	_____ -	_____ =	_____
CHEST	_____ -	_____ =	_____
WAIST	_____ -	_____ =	_____
HIPS	_____ -	_____ =	_____
THIGHS	_____ -	_____ =	_____
CALVES	_____ -	_____ =	_____
ANKLES	_____ -	_____ =	_____

Aerobic Activity:

Intensity level: 1 2 3 4 5 6 7 8 9 10

Duration: _____ **Final pulse:** _____

DATE	START	FINISH	DURATION

Increase/Decrease Intensity

SET 1 | SET 2 | SET 3 | SET 4 | SET 5 | SET 6

@

Training Log

DATE	START	FINISH	DURATION

Aerobic Activity:

Intensity level: 1 2 3 4 5 6 7 8 9 10

Duration: _____ **Final pulse:** _____

	SET 1	SET 2	SET 3	SET 4	SET 5	SET 6
	@	@	@	@	@	@
	@	@	@	@	@	@
	@	@	@	@	@	@
	@	@	@	@	@	@
	@	@	@	@	@	@
	@	@	@	@	@	@
	@	@	@	@	@	@
	@	@	@	@	@	@
	@	@	@	@	@	@
	@	@	@	@	@	@

Increase/Decrease Intensity

Aerobic Activity:

Intensity level: 1 2 3 4 5 6 7 8 9 10

Duration: *Final pulse:*

DATE	START	FINISH	DURATION

Increase/Decrease Intensity

SET 1	SET 2	SET 3	SET 4	SET 5	SET 6

Training Log

DATE	START	FINISH	DURATION

Aerobic Activity:

Intensity level: 1 2 3 4 5 6 7 8 9 10

Duration: _____ **Final pulse:** _____

SET 1	SET 2	SET 3	SET 4	SET 5	SET 6
@	@	@	@	@	@
@	@	@	@	@	@
@	@	@	@	@	@
@	@	@	@	@	@
@	@	@	@	@	@
@	@	@	@	@	@
@	@	@	@	@	@
@	@	@	@	@	@
@	@	@	@	@	@
@	@	@	@	@	@

Increase/Decrease Intensity

Aerobic Activity:

Intensity level: 1 2 3 4 5 6 7 8 9 10

Duration: _____ **Final pulse:** _____

DATE	START	FINISH	DURATION

	SET 1	SET 2	SET 3	SET 4	SET 5	SET 6
	@	@	@	@	@	@
	@	@	@	@	@	@
	@	@	@	@	@	@
	@	@	@	@	@	@
	@	@	@	@	@	@
	@	@	@	@	@	@
	@	@	@	@	@	@
	@	@	@	@	@	@
	@	@	@	@	@	@
	@	@	@	@	@	@

Increase/Decrease Intensity

135

Training Log

DATE	START	FINISH	DURATION

Aerobic Activity:

Intensity level: 1 2 3 4 5 6 7 8 9 10

Duration: **Final pulse:**

SET 1	SET 2	SET 3	SET 4	SET 5	SET 6
@	@	@	@	@	@
@	@	@	@	@	@
@	@	@	@	@	@
@	@	@	@	@	@
@	@	@	@	@	@
@	@	@	@	@	@
@	@	@	@	@	@
@	@	@	@	@	@
@	@	@	@	@	@
@	@	@	@	@	@

Increase/Decrease Intensity

Aerobic Activity:

Intensity level: 1 2 3 4 5 6 7 8 9 10

Duration: _Final pulse:_

DATE	START	FINISH	DURATION

Increase/Decrease Intensity

SET 1 | SET 2 | SET 3 | SET 4 | SET 5 | SET 6

@ @ @ @ @ @ @ @ @ @

Training Log

DATE	START	FINISH	DURATION

Aerobic Activity:

Intensity level: 1 2 3 4 5 6 7 8 9 10

Duration: _____ **Final pulse:** _____

SET 1	SET 2	SET 3	SET 4	SET 5	SET 6

Increase/Decrease Intensity

Aerobic Activity:

Intensity level: 1 2 3 4 5 6 7 8 9 10

Duration: **Final pulse:**

DATE	START	FINISH	DURATION

	SET 1	SET 2	SET 3	SET 4	SET 5	SET 6
Increase/Decrease Intensity	@	@	@	@	@	@
	@	@	@	@	@	@
	@	@	@	@	@	@
	@	@	@	@	@	@
	@	@	@	@	@	@
	@	@	@	@	@	@
	@	@	@	@	@	@
	@	@	@	@	@	@
	@	@	@	@	@	@
	@	@	@	@	@	@
	@	@	@	@	@	@

Training Log

DATE	START	FINISH	DURATION

Aerobic Activity:

Intensity level: 1 2 3 4 5 6 7 8 9 10

Duration: **Final pulse:**

	SET 1	SET 2	SET 3	SET 4	SET 5	SET 6
	@	@	@	@	@	@
	@	@	@	@	@	@
	@	@	@	@	@	@
	@	@	@	@	@	@
	@	@	@	@	@	@
	@	@	@	@	@	@
	@	@	@	@	@	@
	@	@	@	@	@	@
	@	@	@	@	@	@
	@	@	@	@	@	@
	@	@	@	@	@	@

Increase/Decrease Intensity

Aerobic Activity:

Intensity level: 1 2 3 4 5 6 7 8 9 10

Duration: *Final pulse:*

DATE	START	FINISH	DURATION

SET 1   SET 2   SET 3   SET 4   SET 5   SET 6

Increase/Decrease Intensity

Training Log

DATE	START	FINISH	DURATION

Increase/Decrease Intensity

	SET 1	SET 2	SET 3	SET 4	SET 5	SET 6
	@	@	@	@	@	@
	@	@	@	@	@	@
	@	@	@	@	@	@
	@	@	@	@	@	@
	@	@	@	@	@	@
	@	@	@	@	@	@
	@	@	@	@	@	@
	@	@	@	@	@	@
	@	@	@	@	@	@
	@	@	@	@	@	@
	@	@	@	@	@	@

Aerobic Activity:

Intensity level: 1 2 3 4 5 6 7 8 9 10

Duration: *Final pulse:*

DATE	START	FINISH	DURATION

	SET 1	SET 2	SET 3	SET 4	SET 5	SET 6

Increase/Decrease Intensity

Training Log

DATE	START	FINISH	DURATION

Aerobic Activity:

Intensity level: 1 2 3 4 5 6 7 8 9 10

Duration: **Final pulse:**

Increase/Decrease Intensity

SET 1   SET 2   SET 3   SET 4   SET 5   SET 6

@   @   @   @   @   @

@   @   @   @   @   @

@   @   @   @   @   @

@   @   @   @   @   @

@   @   @   @   @   @

@   @   @   @   @   @

@   @   @   @   @   @

@   @   @   @   @   @

@   @   @   @   @   @

@   @   @   @   @   @

Aerobic Activity:

Intensity level: 1 2 3 4 5 6 7 8 9 10

Duration: **Final pulse:**

DATE	START	FINISH	DURATION

SET 1   SET 2   SET 3   SET 4   SET 5   SET 6

Increase/Decrease Intensity

Training Log

DATE	START	FINISH	DURATION

Increase/Decrease Intensity

SET 1	SET 2	SET 3	SET 4	SET 5	SET 6
@	@	@	@	@	@
@	@	@	@	@	@
@	@	@	@	@	@
@	@	@	@	@	@
@	@	@	@	@	@
@	@	@	@	@	@
@	@	@	@	@	@
@	@	@	@	@	@
@	@	@	@	@	@
@	@	@	@	@	@
@	@	@	@	@	@

Aerobic Activity:

Intensity level: 1 2 3 4 5 6 7 8 9 10

Duration: **Final pulse:**

DATE	START	FINISH	DURATION

	SET 1	SET 2	SET 3	SET 4	SET 5	SET 6
Increase/Decrease Intensity	@	@	@	@	@	@
	@	@	@	@	@	@
	@	@	@	@	@	@
	@	@	@	@	@	@
	@	@	@	@	@	@
	@	@	@	@	@	@
	@	@	@	@	@	@
	@	@	@	@	@	@
	@	@	@	@	@	@
	@	@	@	@	@	@
	@	@	@	@	@	@

Training Log

DATE	START	FINISH	DURATION

Aerobic Activity:

Intensity level: 1 2 3 4 5 6 7 8 9 10

Duration: **Final pulse:**

Increase/Decrease Intensity

SET 1	SET 2	SET 3	SET 4	SET 5	SET 6
@	@	@	@	@	@
@	@	@	@	@	@
@	@	@	@	@	@
@	@	@	@	@	@
@	@	@	@	@	@
@	@	@	@	@	@
@	@	@	@	@	@
@	@	@	@	@	@
@	@	@	@	@	@
@	@	@	@	@	@

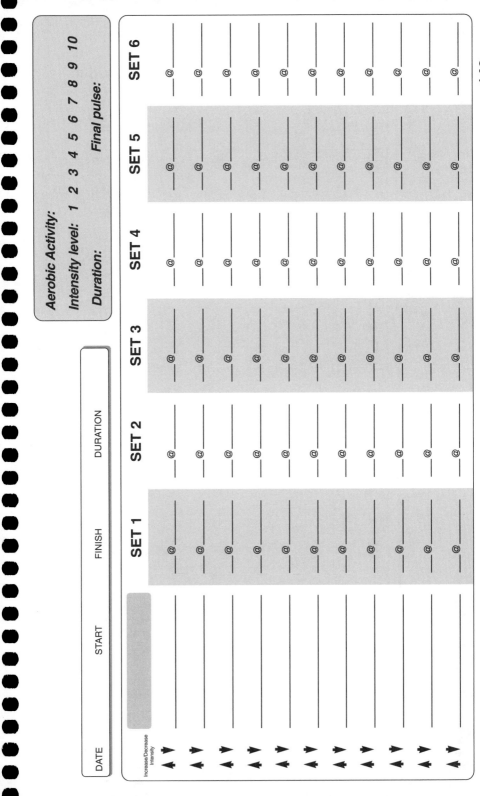

Aerobic Activity:

Intensity level: 1 2 3 4 5 6 7 8 9 10

Duration: Final pulse:

DATE	START	FINISH	DURATION

Increase/Decrease Intensity

SET 1   SET 2   SET 3   SET 4   SET 5   SET 6

Training Log

DATE	START	FINISH	DURATION

Increase/Decrease
Intensity

Aerobic Activity:

Intensity level: 1 2 3 4 5 6 7 8 9 10

Duration: _____ **Final pulse:** _____

SET 1	SET 2	SET 3	SET 4	SET 5	SET 6
@	@	@	@	@	@
@	@	@	@	@	@
@	@	@	@	@	@
@	@	@	@	@	@
@	@	@	@	@	@
@	@	@	@	@	@
@	@	@	@	@	@
@	@	@	@	@	@
@	@	@	@	@	@
@	@	@	@	@	@

Aerobic Activity:

Intensity level: *1 2 3 4 5 6 7 8 9 10*

Final pulse:

Duration:

DATE	START	FINISH	DURATION

SET 1	SET 2	SET 3	SET 4	SET 5	SET 6

Increase/Decrease Intensity

Training Log

DATE	START	FINISH	DURATION

Aerobic Activity:

Intensity level: 1 2 3 4 5 6 7 8 9 10

Duration: **Final pulse:**

Increase/Decrease Intensity

SET 1	SET 2	SET 3	SET 4	SET 5	SET 6
@	@	@	@	@	@
@	@	@	@	@	@
@	@	@	@	@	@
@	@	@	@	@	@
@	@	@	@	@	@
@	@	@	@	@	@
@	@	@	@	@	@
@	@	@	@	@	@
@	@	@	@	@	@
@	@	@	@	@	@

Aerobic Activity:

Intensity level: 1 2 3 4 5 6 7 8 9 10

Duration: _____ *Final pulse:* _____

DATE	START	FINISH	DURATION

	SET 1	SET 2	SET 3	SET 4	SET 5	SET 6
Increase/Decrease Intensity						

Training Log

DATE	START	FINISH	DURATION

Increase/Decrease Intensity

SET 1	SET 2	SET 3	SET 4	SET 5	SET 6
@	@	@	@	@	@
@	@	@	@	@	@
@	@	@	@	@	@
@	@	@	@	@	@
@	@	@	@	@	@
@	@	@	@	@	@
@	@	@	@	@	@
@	@	@	@	@	@
@	@	@	@	@	@
@	@	@	@	@	@

Aerobic Activity:

Intensity level: 1 2 3 4 5 6 7 8 9 10

Duration: **Final pulse:**

DATE	START	FINISH	DURATION

	SET 1	SET 2	SET 3	SET 4	SET 5	SET 6

Increase/Decrease Intensity

@ @ @ @ @ @
@ @ @ @ @ @
@ @ @ @ @ @
@ @ @ @ @ @
@ @ @ @ @ @
@ @ @ @ @ @
@ @ @ @ @ @
@ @ @ @ @ @
@ @ @ @ @ @
@ @ @ @ @ @

155

Training Log

DATE	START	FINISH	DURATION

Aerobic Activity:

Intensity level: 1 2 3 4 5 6 7 8 9 10

Duration: **Final pulse:**

Increase/Decrease Intensity

SET 1	SET 2	SET 3	SET 4	SET 5	SET 6
@	@	@	@	@	@
@	@	@	@	@	@
@	@	@	@	@	@
@	@	@	@	@	@
@	@	@	@	@	@
@	@	@	@	@	@
@	@	@	@	@	@
@	@	@	@	@	@
@	@	@	@	@	@
@	@	@	@	@	@

Aerobic Activity:

Intensity level: 1 2 3 4 5 6 7 8 9 10

Duration: _____ **Final pulse:** _____

DATE	START	FINISH	DURATION

Increase/Decrease Intensity

SET 1   SET 2   SET 3   SET 4   SET 5   SET 6

Training Log

DATE	START	FINISH	DURATION

Aerobic Activity:

Intensity level: 1 2 3 4 5 6 7 8 9 10

Duration: **Final pulse:**

Increase/Decrease Intensity

SET 1	SET 2	SET 3	SET 4	SET 5	SET 6
@	@	@	@	@	@
@	@	@	@	@	@
@	@	@	@	@	@
@	@	@	@	@	@
@	@	@	@	@	@
@	@	@	@	@	@
@	@	@	@	@	@
@	@	@	@	@	@
@	@	@	@	@	@
@	@	@	@	@	@

EVALUATION
PAGE

DATE: **BODY WEIGHT:**

STRENGTH

Exercises	LAST WORKOUT	FIRST W/O	GAIN
#1	_____ -	_____ =	_____
#2	_____ -	_____ =	_____
#3	_____ -	_____ =	_____
#4	_____ -	_____ =	_____
#5	_____ -	_____ =	_____
#6	_____ -	_____ =	_____
#7	_____ -	_____ =	_____
#8	_____ -	_____ =	_____

SIZE

	ACTUAL	GOAL	DIFFERENCE
NECK	_____ -	_____ =	_____
BICEPS	_____ -	_____ =	_____
FOREARMS	_____ -	_____ =	_____
CHEST	_____ -	_____ =	_____
WAIST	_____ -	_____ =	_____
HIPS	_____ -	_____ =	_____
THIGHS	_____ -	_____ =	_____
CALVES	_____ -	_____ =	_____
ANKLES	_____ -	_____ =	_____

159

Training Log

DATE	START	FINISH	DURATION

Aerobic Activity:

Intensity level: 1 2 3 4 5 6 7 8 9 10

Duration: **Final pulse:**

Increase/Decrease Intensity

SET 1	SET 2	SET 3	SET 4	SET 5	SET 6
@	@	@	@	@	@
@	@	@	@	@	@
@	@	@	@	@	@
@	@	@	@	@	@
@	@	@	@	@	@
@	@	@	@	@	@
@	@	@	@	@	@
@	@	@	@	@	@
@	@	@	@	@	@
@	@	@	@	@	@
@	@	@	@	@	@

Aerobic Activity:

Intensity level: 1 2 3 4 5 6 7 8 9 10

Duration: **Final pulse:**

DATE	START	FINISH	DURATION

Increase/Decrease Intensity

SET 1 SET 2 SET 3 SET 4 SET 5 SET 6

Training Log

Aerobic Activity:

Intensity level: 1 2 3 4 5 6 7 8 9 10

Duration: **Final pulse:**

Increase/Decrease Intensity	SET 1	SET 2	SET 3	SET 4	SET 5	SET 6
	@	@	@	@	@	@
	@	@	@	@	@	@
	@	@	@	@	@	@
	@	@	@	@	@	@
	@	@	@	@	@	@
	@	@	@	@	@	@
	@	@	@	@	@	@
	@	@	@	@	@	@
	@	@	@	@	@	@
	@	@	@	@	@	@

Aerobic Activity:

Intensity level: 1 2 3 4 5 6 7 8 9 10

Duration: **Final pulse:**

DATE	START	FINISH	DURATION

SET 1 SET 2 SET 3 SET 4 SET 5 SET 6

Increase/Decrease
Intensity

@ @ @ @ @ @
@ @ @ @ @ @
@ @ @ @ @ @
@ @ @ @ @ @
@ @ @ @ @ @
@ @ @ @ @ @
@ @ @ @ @ @
@ @ @ @ @ @
@ @ @ @ @ @
@ @ @ @ @ @

Training Log

DATE	START	FINISH	DURATION

Aerobic Activity:

Intensity level: 1 2 3 4 5 6 7 8 9 10

Duration: **Final pulse:**

Increase/Decrease Intensity

SET 1	SET 2	SET 3	SET 4	SET 5	SET 6
@	@	@	@	@	@
@	@	@	@	@	@
@	@	@	@	@	@
@	@	@	@	@	@
@	@	@	@	@	@
@	@	@	@	@	@
@	@	@	@	@	@
@	@	@	@	@	@
@	@	@	@	@	@
@	@	@	@	@	@

Aerobic Activity:

Intensity level: 1 2 3 4 5 6 7 8 9 10

Duration: **Final pulse:**

DATE	START	FINISH	DURATION

Increase/Decrease Intensity

SET 1	SET 2	SET 3	SET 4	SET 5	SET 6
@	@	@	@	@	@
@	@	@	@	@	@
@	@	@	@	@	@
@	@	@	@	@	@
@	@	@	@	@	@
@	@	@	@	@	@
@	@	@	@	@	@
@	@	@	@	@	@
@	@	@	@	@	@
@	@	@	@	@	@

Training Log

DATE	START	FINISH	DURATION

Aerobic Activity:

Intensity level: 1 2 3 4 5 6 7 8 9 10

Duration: _____ **Final pulse:** _____

Increase/Decrease Intensity

SET 1	SET 2	SET 3	SET 4	SET 5	SET 6
@	@	@	@	@	@
@	@	@	@	@	@
@	@	@	@	@	@
@	@	@	@	@	@
@	@	@	@	@	@
@	@	@	@	@	@
@	@	@	@	@	@
@	@	@	@	@	@
@	@	@	@	@	@
@	@	@	@	@	@

Aerobic Activity:

Intensity level: 1 2 3 4 5 6 7 8 9 10

Duration: *Final pulse:*

DATE	START	FINISH	DURATION

	SET 1	SET 2	SET 3	SET 4	SET 5	SET 6
Increase/Decrease Intensity	@	@	@	@	@	@
	@	@	@	@	@	@
	@	@	@	@	@	@
	@	@	@	@	@	@
	@	@	@	@	@	@
	@	@	@	@	@	@
	@	@	@	@	@	@
	@	@	@	@	@	@
	@	@	@	@	@	@
	@	@	@	@	@	@

Training Log

DATE	START	FINISH	DURATION

Aerobic Activity:

Intensity level: 1 2 3 4 5 6 7 8 9 10

Duration: _____ **Final pulse:** _____

	SET 1	SET 2	SET 3	SET 4	SET 5	SET 6
	@	@	@	@	@	@
	@	@	@	@	@	@
	@	@	@	@	@	@
	@	@	@	@	@	@
	@	@	@	@	@	@
	@	@	@	@	@	@
	@	@	@	@	@	@
	@	@	@	@	@	@
	@	@	@	@	@	@
	@	@	@	@	@	@
	@	@	@	@	@	@

Increase/Decrease Intensity

Aerobic Activity:

Intensity level: 1 2 3 4 5 6 7 8 9 10

Duration: _____ **Final pulse:** _____

DATE	START	FINISH	DURATION

Increase/Decrease Intensity

	SET 1	SET 2	SET 3	SET 4	SET 5	SET 6
	@	@	@	@	@	@
	@	@	@	@	@	@
	@	@	@	@	@	@
	@	@	@	@	@	@
	@	@	@	@	@	@
	@	@	@	@	@	@
	@	@	@	@	@	@
	@	@	@	@	@	@
	@	@	@	@	@	@
	@	@	@	@	@	@
	@	@	@	@	@	@

Training Log

DATE	START	FINISH	DURATION

Aerobic Activity:

Intensity level: 1 2 3 4 5 6 7 8 9 10

Duration: **Final pulse:**

Increase/Decrease Intensity

	SET 1	SET 2	SET 3	SET 4	SET 5	SET 6
	@	@	@	@	@	@
	@	@	@	@	@	@
	@	@	@	@	@	@
	@	@	@	@	@	@
	@	@	@	@	@	@
	@	@	@	@	@	@
	@	@	@	@	@	@
	@	@	@	@	@	@
	@	@	@	@	@	@
	@	@	@	@	@	@

Aerobic Activity:

Intensity level: 1 2 3 4 5 6 7 8 9 10

Duration: *Final pulse:*

DATE	START	FINISH	DURATION

Increase/Decrease Intensity

SET 1 SET 2 SET 3 SET 4 SET 5 SET 6

@ @ @ @ @ @
@ @ @ @ @ @
@ @ @ @ @ @
@ @ @ @ @ @
@ @ @ @ @ @
@ @ @ @ @ @
@ @ @ @ @ @
@ @ @ @ @ @
@ @ @ @ @ @
@ @ @ @ @ @

171

Training Log

DATE	START	FINISH	DURATION

Aerobic Activity:

Intensity level: 1 2 3 4 5 6 7 8 9 10

Duration: **Final pulse:**

Increase/Decrease Intensity	SET 1	SET 2	SET 3	SET 4	SET 5	SET 6
◄ ►	@	@	@	@	@	@
◄ ►	@	@	@	@	@	@
◄ ►	@	@	@	@	@	@
◄ ►	@	@	@	@	@	@
◄ ►	@	@	@	@	@	@
◄ ►	@	@	@	@	@	@
◄ ►	@	@	@	@	@	@
◄ ►	@	@	@	@	@	@
◄ ►	@	@	@	@	@	@
◄ ►	@	@	@	@	@	@

Aerobic Activity:

Intensity level: 1 2 3 4 5 6 7 8 9 10

Duration: _____ *Final pulse:* _____

DATE	START	FINISH	DURATION

Increase/Decrease Intensity

SET 1 SET 2 SET 3 SET 4 SET 5 SET 6

@ @ @ @ @ @
@ @ @ @ @ @
@ @ @ @ @ @
@ @ @ @ @ @
@ @ @ @ @ @
@ @ @ @ @ @
@ @ @ @ @ @
@ @ @ @ @ @
@ @ @ @ @ @
@ @ @ @ @ @
@ @ @ @ @ @

Training Log

DATE	START	FINISH	DURATION

Increase/Decrease Intensity

SET 1   SET 2   SET 3   SET 4   SET 5   SET 6

Aerobic Activity:

Intensity level: 1 2 3 4 5 6 7 8 9 10

Duration: *Final pulse:*

Aerobic Activity:

Intensity level: 1 2 3 4 5 6 7 8 9 10

Duration: **Final pulse:**

DATE	START	FINISH	DURATION

	SET 1	SET 2	SET 3	SET 4	SET 5	SET 6

Increase/Decrease Intensity

Training Log

DATE	START	FINISH	DURATION

Aerobic Activity:

Intensity level: 1 2 3 4 5 6 7 8 9 10

Duration: **Final pulse:**

SET 1	SET 2	SET 3	SET 4	SET 5	SET 6
@	@	@	@	@	@
@	@	@	@	@	@
@	@	@	@	@	@
@	@	@	@	@	@
@	@	@	@	@	@
@	@	@	@	@	@
@	@	@	@	@	@
@	@	@	@	@	@
@	@	@	@	@	@
@	@	@	@	@	@
@	@	@	@	@	@

Increase/Decrease Intensity

Aerobic Activity:

Intensity level: 1 2 3 4 5 6 7 8 9 10

Final pulse:

Duration:

DATE	START	FINISH	DURATION

	SET 1	SET 2	SET 3	SET 4	SET 5	SET 6

Increase/Decrease Intensity

Training Log

DATE	START	FINISH	DURATION

Increase/Decrease Intensity

SET 1 @

SET 2 @

SET 3 @

SET 4 @

SET 5 @

SET 6 @

Aerobic Activity:

Intensity level: 1 2 3 4 5 6 7 8 9 10

Duration: Final pulse:

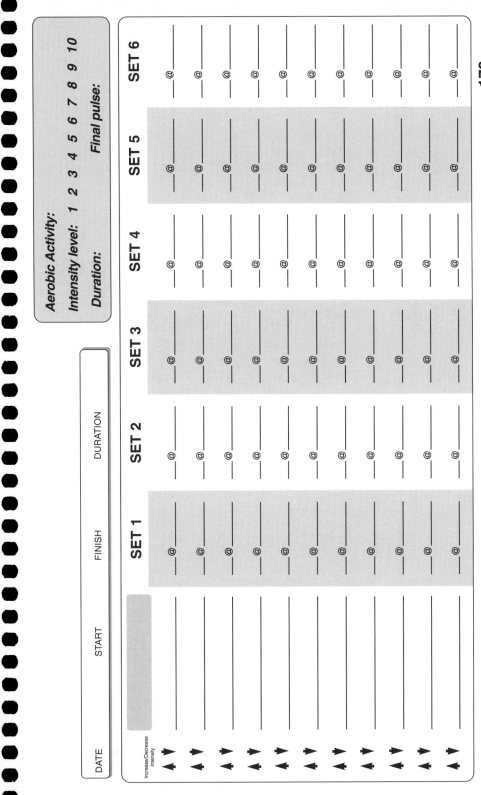

Aerobic Activity:

Intensity level: 1 2 3 4 5 6 7 8 9 10

Final pulse:

Duration:

DATE   START   FINISH   DURATION

SET 1   SET 2   SET 3   SET 4   SET 5   SET 6

Increase/Decrease Intensity

Training Log

DATE	START	FINISH	DURATION

Aerobic Activity:

Intensity level: 1 2 3 4 5 6 7 8 9 10

Duration: **Final pulse:**

	SET 1	SET 2	SET 3	SET 4	SET 5	SET 6

Increase/Decrease Intensity

Aerobic Activity:

Intensity level: 1 2 3 4 5 6 7 8 9 10

Duration: ___ **Final pulse:** ___

DATE	START	FINISH	DURATION

	SET 1	SET 2	SET 3	SET 4	SET 5	SET 6
Increase/Decrease Intensity	@	@	@	@	@	@
	@	@	@	@	@	@
	@	@	@	@	@	@
	@	@	@	@	@	@
	@	@	@	@	@	@
	@	@	@	@	@	@
	@	@	@	@	@	@
	@	@	@	@	@	@
	@	@	@	@	@	@
	@	@	@	@	@	@
	@	@	@	@	@	@

Training Log

DATE	START	FINISH	DURATION

Aerobic Activity:

Intensity level: 1 2 3 4 5 6 7 8 9 10

Duration: **Final pulse:**

Increase/Decrease Intensity	SET 1	SET 2	SET 3	SET 4	SET 5	SET 6
◀ ▶	@	@	@	@	@	@
◀ ▶	@	@	@	@	@	@
◀ ▶	@	@	@	@	@	@
◀ ▶	@	@	@	@	@	@
◀ ▶	@	@	@	@	@	@
◀ ▶	@	@	@	@	@	@
◀ ▶	@	@	@	@	@	@
◀ ▶	@	@	@	@	@	@
◀ ▶	@	@	@	@	@	@
◀ ▶	@	@	@	@	@	@

Aerobic Activity:

Intensity level: 1 2 3 4 5 6 7 8 9 10

Duration: **Final pulse:**

DATE	START	FINISH	DURATION

Increase/Decrease Intensity

SET 1	SET 2	SET 3	SET 4	SET 5	SET 6

Training Log

DATE	START	FINISH	DURATION

Aerobic Activity:

Intensity level: 1 2 3 4 5 6 7 8 9 10

Duration: **Final pulse:**

Increase/Decrease Intensity

	SET 1	SET 2	SET 3	SET 4	SET 5	SET 6
↑↓	@	@	@	@	@	@
↑↓	@	@	@	@	@	@
↑↓	@	@	@	@	@	@
↑↓	@	@	@	@	@	@
↑↓	@	@	@	@	@	@
↑↓	@	@	@	@	@	@
↑↓	@	@	@	@	@	@
↑↓	@	@	@	@	@	@
↑↓	@	@	@	@	@	@
↑↓	@	@	@	@	@	@

Aerobic Activity:

Intensity level: 1 2 3 4 5 6 7 8 9 10

Final pulse:

Duration:

DATE	START	FINISH	DURATION

Increase/Decrease Intensity

SET 1	SET 2	SET 3	SET 4	SET 5	SET 6
@	@	@	@	@	@
@	@	@	@	@	@
@	@	@	@	@	@
@	@	@	@	@	@
@	@	@	@	@	@
@	@	@	@	@	@
@	@	@	@	@	@
@	@	@	@	@	@
@	@	@	@	@	@
@	@	@	@	@	@
@	@	@	@	@	@

185

Training Log

DATE	START	FINISH	DURATION

Aerobic Activity:

Intensity level: 1 2 3 4 5 6 7 8 9 10

Duration: **Final pulse:**

	SET 1	SET 2	SET 3	SET 4	SET 5	SET 6

Increase/Decrease Intensity

Aerobic Activity:

Intensity level: 1 2 3 4 5 6 7 8 9 10

Duration: **Final pulse:**

DATE	START	FINISH	DURATION

Increase/Decrease Intensity

SET 1 | SET 2 | SET 3 | SET 4 | SET 5 | SET 6

EVALUATION
PAGE

DATE: BODY WEIGHT:

STRENGTH

Exercises	LAST WORKOUT	FIRST W/O	GAIN
#1	_____ -	_____ =	_____
#2	_____ -	_____ =	_____
#3	_____ -	_____ =	_____
#4	_____ -	_____ =	_____
#5	_____ -	_____ =	_____
#6	_____ -	_____ =	_____
#7	_____ -	_____ =	_____
#8	_____ -	_____ =	_____

SIZE

SIZE	ACTUAL	GOAL	DIFFERENCE
NECK	_____ -	_____ =	_____
BICEPS	_____ -	_____ =	_____
FOREARMS	_____ -	_____ =	_____
CHEST	_____ -	_____ =	_____
WAIST	_____ -	_____ =	_____
HIPS	_____ -	_____ =	_____
THIGHS	_____ -	_____ =	_____
CALVES	_____ -	_____ =	_____
ANKLES	_____ -	_____ =	_____

Aerobic Activity:

Intensity level: 1 2 3 4 5 6 7 8 9 10

Duration: **Final pulse:**

DATE	START	FINISH	DURATION

SET 1   SET 2   SET 3   SET 4   SET 5   SET 6

Increase/Decrease
Intensity

189

Training Log

DATE	START	FINISH	DURATION

Aerobic Activity:

Intensity level: 1 2 3 4 5 6 7 8 9 10

Duration: _____ **Final pulse:** _____

	SET 1	SET 2	SET 3	SET 4	SET 5	SET 6
	@	@	@	@	@	@
	@	@	@	@	@	@
	@	@	@	@	@	@
	@	@	@	@	@	@
	@	@	@	@	@	@
	@	@	@	@	@	@
	@	@	@	@	@	@
	@	@	@	@	@	@
	@	@	@	@	@	@
	@	@	@	@	@	@
	@	@	@	@	@	@

Increase/Decrease Intensity

Aerobic Activity:

Intensity level: 1 2 3 4 5 6 7 8 9 10

Duration: **Final pulse:**

DATE	START	FINISH	DURATION

SET 1   SET 2   SET 3   SET 4   SET 5   SET 6

@   @   @   @   @   @

Increase/Decrease Intensity

Training Log

DATE	START	FINISH	DURATION

Aerobic Activity:

Intensity level: 1 2 3 4 5 6 7 8 9 10

Duration: _____ **Final pulse:** _____

Increase/Decrease Intensity

SET 1 SET 2 SET 3 SET 4 SET 5 SET 6

Aerobic Activity:

Intensity level: 1 2 3 4 5 6 7 8 9 10

Duration: _____ **Final pulse:** _____

DATE	START	FINISH	DURATION

	SET 1	SET 2	SET 3	SET 4	SET 5	SET 6

Increase/Decrease Intensity

Training Log

DATE	START	FINISH	DURATION

Aerobic Activity:

Intensity level: 1 2 3 4 5 6 7 8 9 10

Duration: **Final pulse:**

Increase/Decrease Intensity

SET 1	SET 2	SET 3	SET 4	SET 5	SET 6
@	@	@	@	@	@
@	@	@	@	@	@
@	@	@	@	@	@
@	@	@	@	@	@
@	@	@	@	@	@
@	@	@	@	@	@
@	@	@	@	@	@
@	@	@	@	@	@
@	@	@	@	@	@
@	@	@	@	@	@
@	@	@	@	@	@

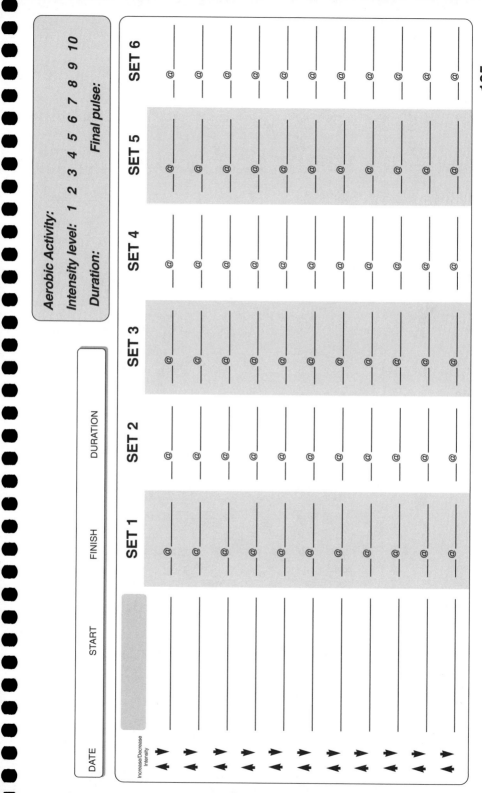

Training Log

DATE	START	FINISH	DURATION

Aerobic Activity:

Intensity level: 1 2 3 4 5 6 7 8 9 10

Duration: **Final pulse:**

	SET 1	SET 2	SET 3	SET 4	SET 5	SET 6

Increase/Decrease Intensity

@

Aerobic Activity:

Intensity level: 1 2 3 4 5 6 7 8 9 10

Duration: **Final pulse:**

DATE	START	FINISH	DURATION

SET 1   SET 2   SET 3   SET 4   SET 5   SET 6

Increase/Decrease Intensity

Training Log

DATE	START	FINISH	DURATION

Aerobic Activity:

Intensity level: 1 2 3 4 5 6 7 8 9 10

Duration: **Final pulse:**

Increase/Decrease Intensity

SET 1	SET 2	SET 3	SET 4	SET 5	SET 6
@	@	@	@	@	@
@	@	@	@	@	@
@	@	@	@	@	@
@	@	@	@	@	@
@	@	@	@	@	@
@	@	@	@	@	@
@	@	@	@	@	@
@	@	@	@	@	@
@	@	@	@	@	@
@	@	@	@	@	@
@	@	@	@	@	@

Aerobic Activity:

Intensity level: *1 2 3 4 5 6 7 8 9 10*

Duration: **Final pulse:**

DATE	START	FINISH	DURATION

	SET 1	SET 2	SET 3	SET 4	SET 5	SET 6

Increase/Decrease Intensity

Training Log

DATE	START	FINISH	DURATION

Aerobic Activity:

Intensity level: 1 2 3 4 5 6 7 8 9 10

Duration: **Final pulse:**

Increase/Decrease Intensity

SET 1   SET 2   SET 3   SET 4   SET 5   SET 6

@   @   @   @   @   @

Aerobic Activity:

Intensity level: 1 2 3 4 5 6 7 8 9 10

Duration: **Final pulse:**

DATE	START	FINISH	DURATION

Increase/Decrease Intensity

SET 1	SET 2	SET 3	SET 4	SET 5	SET 6
@	@	@	@	@	@
@	@	@	@	@	@
@	@	@	@	@	@
@	@	@	@	@	@
@	@	@	@	@	@
@	@	@	@	@	@
@	@	@	@	@	@
@	@	@	@	@	@
@	@	@	@	@	@
@	@	@	@	@	@
@	@	@	@	@	@

201

Training Log

DATE	START	FINISH	DURATION

Aerobic Activity:

Intensity level: 1 2 3 4 5 6 7 8 9 10

Duration: *Final pulse:*

	SET 1	SET 2	SET 3	SET 4	SET 5	SET 6

Increase/Decrease
Intensity

Aerobic Activity:

Intensity level: 1 2 3 4 5 6 7 8 9 10

Duration: _____ **Final pulse:** _____

DATE	START	FINISH	DURATION

	SET 1	SET 2	SET 3	SET 4	SET 5	SET 6
Increase/Decrease Intensity	@	@	@	@	@	@
	@	@	@	@	@	@
	@	@	@	@	@	@
	@	@	@	@	@	@
	@	@	@	@	@	@
	@	@	@	@	@	@
	@	@	@	@	@	@
	@	@	@	@	@	@
	@	@	@	@	@	@
	@	@	@	@	@	@
	@	@	@	@	@	@

Training Log

DATE	START	FINISH	DURATION

Aerobic Activity:

Intensity level: 1 2 3 4 5 6 7 8 9 10

Duration: **Final pulse:**

Increase/Decrease Intensity

SET 1	SET 2	SET 3	SET 4	SET 5	SET 6
@	@	@	@	@	@
@	@	@	@	@	@
@	@	@	@	@	@
@	@	@	@	@	@
@	@	@	@	@	@
@	@	@	@	@	@
@	@	@	@	@	@
@	@	@	@	@	@
@	@	@	@	@	@
@	@	@	@	@	@

Aerobic Activity:

Intensity level: *1 2 3 4 5 6 7 8 9 10*

Duration: _____ **Final pulse:** _____

DATE	START	FINISH	DURATION

	SET 1	SET 2	SET 3	SET 4	SET 5	SET 6
Increase/Decrease Intensity → ←	@	@	@	@	@	@
→ ←	@	@	@	@	@	@
→ ←	@	@	@	@	@	@
→ ←	@	@	@	@	@	@
→ ←	@	@	@	@	@	@
→ ←	@	@	@	@	@	@
→ ←	@	@	@	@	@	@
→ ←	@	@	@	@	@	@
→ ←	@	@	@	@	@	@
→ ←	@	@	@	@	@	@
→ ←	@	@	@	@	@	@

Training Log

DATE	START	FINISH	DURATION

Aerobic Activity:

Intensity level: 1 2 3 4 5 6 7 8 9 10

Duration: **Final pulse:**

	SET 1	SET 2	SET 3	SET 4	SET 5	SET 6
	@	@	@	@	@	@
	@	@	@	@	@	@
	@	@	@	@	@	@
	@	@	@	@	@	@
	@	@	@	@	@	@
	@	@	@	@	@	@
	@	@	@	@	@	@
	@	@	@	@	@	@
	@	@	@	@	@	@
	@	@	@	@	@	@

Increase/Decrease Intensity

Aerobic Activity:

Intensity level: 1 2 3 4 5 6 7 8 9 10

Duration: *Final pulse:*

DATE	START	FINISH	DURATION

Increase/Decrease Intensity

	SET 1	SET 2	SET 3	SET 4	SET 5	SET 6
	@	@	@	@	@	@
	@	@	@	@	@	@
	@	@	@	@	@	@
	@	@	@	@	@	@
	@	@	@	@	@	@
	@	@	@	@	@	@
	@	@	@	@	@	@
	@	@	@	@	@	@
	@	@	@	@	@	@
	@	@	@	@	@	@
	@	@	@	@	@	@

Training Log

DATE	START	FINISH	DURATION

Aerobic Activity:

Intensity level: 1 2 3 4 5 6 7 8 9 10

Duration: *Final pulse:*

SET 1	SET 2	SET 3	SET 4	SET 5	SET 6
@	@	@	@	@	@
@	@	@	@	@	@
@	@	@	@	@	@
@	@	@	@	@	@
@	@	@	@	@	@
@	@	@	@	@	@
@	@	@	@	@	@
@	@	@	@	@	@
@	@	@	@	@	@
@	@	@	@	@	@

Increase/Decrease
Intensity

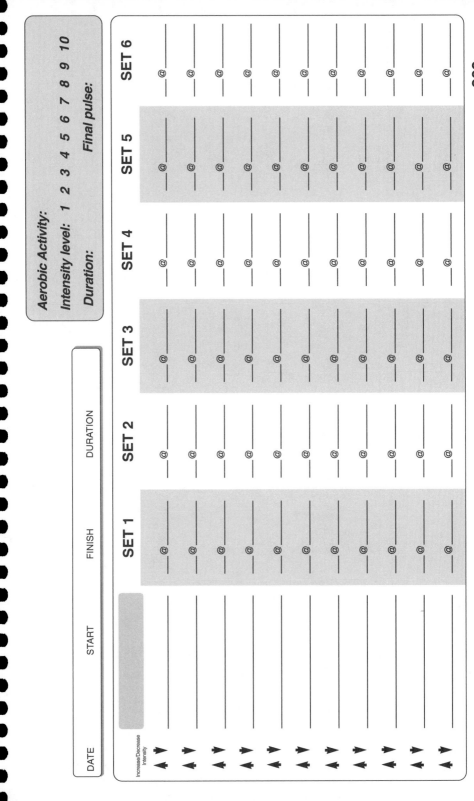

Aerobic Activity:

Intensity level: 1 2 3 4 5 6 7 8 9 10

Final pulse:

Duration:

| DATE | START | FINISH | DURATION |

Increase/Decrease Intensity

SET 1   SET 2   SET 3   SET 4   SET 5   SET 6

Training Log

DATE	START	FINISH	DURATION

Aerobic Activity:

Intensity level: 1 2 3 4 5 6 7 8 9 10

Duration: **Final pulse:**

Increase/Decrease Intensity

SET 1	SET 2	SET 3	SET 4	SET 5	SET 6
@	@	@	@	@	@
@	@	@	@	@	@
@	@	@	@	@	@
@	@	@	@	@	@
@	@	@	@	@	@
@	@	@	@	@	@
@	@	@	@	@	@
@	@	@	@	@	@
@	@	@	@	@	@
@	@	@	@	@	@

Aerobic Activity:

Intensity level: *1 2 3 4 5 6 7 8 9 10*

Duration: *Final pulse:*

DATE	START	FINISH	DURATION

Increase/Decrease Intensity

SET 1	SET 2	SET 3	SET 4	SET 5	SET 6

Training Log

DATE	START	FINISH	DURATION

Aerobic Activity:

Intensity level: 1 2 3 4 5 6 7 8 9 10

Duration: **Final pulse:**

Increase/Decrease Intensity

	SET 1	SET 2	SET 3	SET 4	SET 5	SET 6
	@	@	@	@	@	@
	@	@	@	@	@	@
	@	@	@	@	@	@
	@	@	@	@	@	@
	@	@	@	@	@	@
	@	@	@	@	@	@
	@	@	@	@	@	@
	@	@	@	@	@	@
	@	@	@	@	@	@
	@	@	@	@	@	@

Aerobic Activity:

Intensity level: 1 2 3 4 5 6 7 8 9 10

Duration: **Final pulse:**

DATE	START	FINISH	DURATION

	SET 1	SET 2	SET 3	SET 4	SET 5	SET 6
	@	@	@	@	@	@
	@	@	@	@	@	@
	@	@	@	@	@	@
	@	@	@	@	@	@
	@	@	@	@	@	@
	@	@	@	@	@	@
	@	@	@	@	@	@
	@	@	@	@	@	@
	@	@	@	@	@	@
	@	@	@	@	@	@
	@	@	@	@	@	@

Increase/Decrease Intensity

Training Log

DATE	START	FINISH	DURATION

Aerobic Activity:

Intensity level: 1 2 3 4 5 6 7 8 9 10

Duration: **Final pulse:**

	SET 1	SET 2	SET 3	SET 4	SET 5	SET 6

Increase/Decrease Intensity

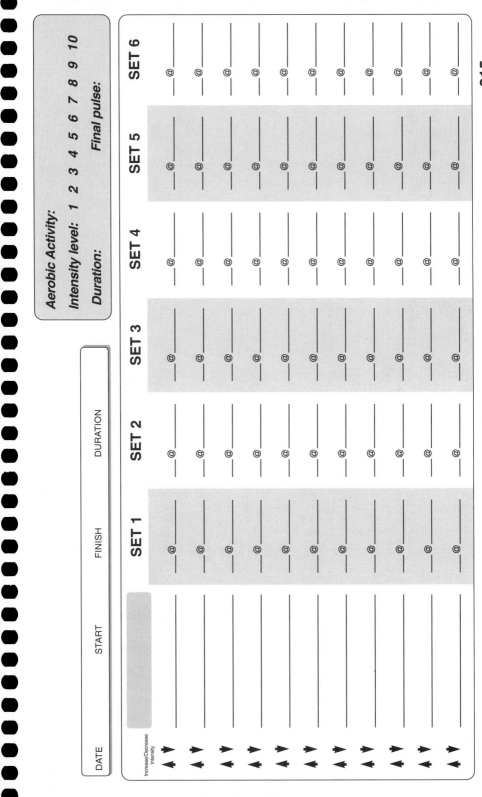

Aerobic Activity:

Intensity level: 1 2 3 4 5 6 7 8 9 10

Duration: Final pulse:

DATE START FINISH DURATION

SET 1 SET 2 SET 3 SET 4 SET 5 SET 6

Increase/Decrease Intensity

215

Training Log

DATE	START	FINISH	DURATION

Aerobic Activity:

Intensity level: 1 2 3 4 5 6 7 8 9 10

Duration: _____ **Final pulse:** _____

Increase/Decrease Intensity

SET 1	SET 2	SET 3	SET 4	SET 5	SET 6
@	@	@	@	@	@
@	@	@	@	@	@
@	@	@	@	@	@
@	@	@	@	@	@
@	@	@	@	@	@
@	@	@	@	@	@
@	@	@	@	@	@
@	@	@	@	@	@
@	@	@	@	@	@
@	@	@	@	@	@
					@

EVALUATION
PAGE

DATE: **BODY WEIGHT:**

STRENGTH

Exercises	LAST WORKOUT	FIRST W/O	GAIN
#1	_____ -	_____ =	_____
#2	_____ -	_____ =	_____
#3	_____ -	_____ =	_____
#4	_____ -	_____ =	_____
#5	_____ -	_____ =	_____
#6	_____ -	_____ =	_____
#7	_____ -	_____ =	_____
#8	_____ -	_____ =	_____

SIZE	ACTUAL	GOAL	DIFFERENCE
NECK	_____ -	_____ =	_____
BICEPS	_____ -	_____ =	_____
FOREARMS	_____ -	_____ =	_____
CHEST	_____ -	_____ =	_____
WAIST	_____ -	_____ =	_____
HIPS	_____ -	_____ =	_____
THIGHS	_____ -	_____ =	_____
CALVES	_____ -	_____ =	_____
ANKLES	_____ -	_____ =	_____

Training Log

DATE	START	FINISH	DURATION

Aerobic Activity:

Intensity level: 1 2 3 4 5 6 7 8 9 10

Duration: **Final pulse:**

Increase/Decrease Intensity

SET 1	SET 2	SET 3	SET 4	SET 5	SET 6
@	@	@	@	@	@
@	@	@	@	@	@
@	@	@	@	@	@
@	@	@	@	@	@
@	@	@	@	@	@
@	@	@	@	@	@
@	@	@	@	@	@
@	@	@	@	@	@
@	@	@	@	@	@
@	@	@	@	@	@

Aerobic Activity:

Intensity level: 1 2 3 4 5 6 7 8 9 10

Duration: **Final pulse:**

DATE	START	FINISH	DURATION

	SET 1	SET 2	SET 3	SET 4	SET 5	SET 6

Increase/Decrease Intensity

@ @ @ @ @ @

@ @ @ @ @ @

@ @ @ @ @ @

@ @ @ @ @ @

@ @ @ @ @ @

@ @ @ @ @ @

@ @ @ @ @ @

@ @ @ @ @ @

@ @ @ @ @ @

@ @ @ @ @ @

@ @ @ @ @ @

Training Log

DATE	START	FINISH	DURATION

Increase/Decrease Intensity

SET 1   SET 2   SET 3   SET 4   SET 5   SET 6

@ @ @ @ @ @ @ @ @ @ @

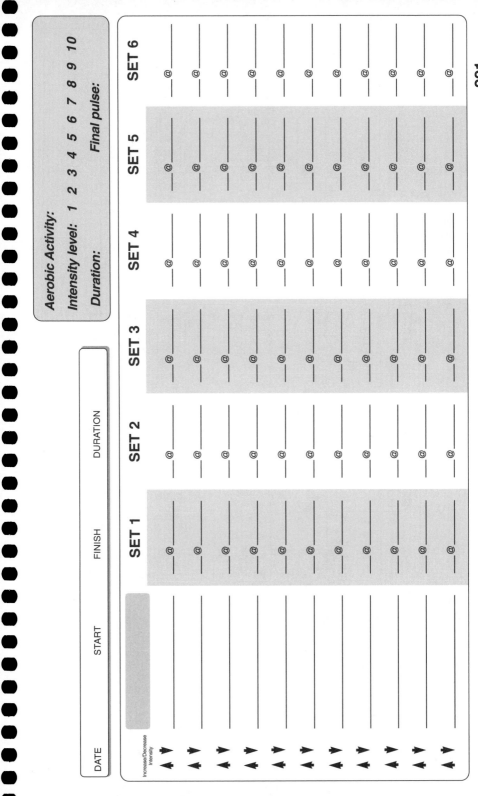

Aerobic Activity:

Intensity level: 1 2 3 4 5 6 7 8 9 10

Duration: _____ Final pulse: _____

DATE	START	FINISH	DURATION

Increase/Decrease Intensity

SET 1   SET 2   SET 3   SET 4   SET 5   SET 6

@

221

Training Log

DATE	START	FINISH	DURATION

Aerobic Activity:

Intensity level: 1 2 3 4 5 6 7 8 9 10

Duration: **Final pulse:**

Increase/Decrease Intensity

SET 1   SET 2   SET 3   SET 4   SET 5   SET 6

@
@
@
@
@
@
@
@
@
@

Aerobic Activity:

Intensity level: 1 2 3 4 5 6 7 8 9 10

Duration: Final pulse:

DATE	START	FINISH	DURATION

Increase/Decrease Intensity

SET 1   SET 2   SET 3   SET 4   SET 5   SET 6

@   @   @   @   @   @
@   @   @   @   @   @
@   @   @   @   @   @
@   @   @   @   @   @
@   @   @   @   @   @
@   @   @   @   @   @
@   @   @   @   @   @
@   @   @   @   @   @
@   @   @   @   @   @
@   @   @   @   @   @
@   @   @   @   @   @

Training Log

DATE	START	FINISH	DURATION

Aerobic Activity:

Intensity level: 1 2 3 4 5 6 7 8 9 10

Duration: _____ **Final pulse:** _____

SET 1	SET 2	SET 3	SET 4	SET 5	SET 6
@	@	@	@	@	@
@	@	@	@	@	@
@	@	@	@	@	@
@	@	@	@	@	@
@	@	@	@	@	@
@	@	@	@	@	@
@	@	@	@	@	@
@	@	@	@	@	@
@	@	@	@	@	@
@	@	@	@	@	@
@	@	@	@	@	@

Increase/Decrease Intensity

Aerobic Activity:

Intensity level: 1 2 3 4 5 6 7 8 9 10

Duration: **Final pulse:**

DATE	START	FINISH	DURATION

Increase/Decrease Intensity

	SET 1	SET 2	SET 3	SET 4	SET 5	SET 6

@ @ @ @ @ @
@ @ @ @ @ @
@ @ @ @ @ @
@ @ @ @ @ @
@ @ @ @ @ @
@ @ @ @ @ @
@ @ @ @ @ @
@ @ @ @ @ @
@ @ @ @ @ @
@ @ @ @ @ @
@ @ @ @ @ @

Training Log

DATE	START	FINISH	DURATION

Aerobic Activity:

Intensity level: 1 2 3 4 5 6 7 8 9 10

Duration: **Final pulse:**

	SET 1	SET 2	SET 3	SET 4	SET 5	SET 6

Increase/Decrease Intensity

Aerobic Activity:

Intensity level: 1 2 3 4 5 6 7 8 9 10

Duration: **Final pulse:**

DATE	START	FINISH	DURATION

	SET 1	SET 2	SET 3	SET 4	SET 5	SET 6

Increase/Decrease Intensity

Training Log

DATE	START	FINISH	DURATION

Aerobic Activity:

Intensity level: 1 2 3 4 5 6 7 8 9 10

Duration: **Final pulse:**

	SET 1	SET 2	SET 3	SET 4	SET 5	SET 6

Increase/Decrease Intensity

Aerobic Activity:

Intensity level: 1 2 3 4 5 6 7 8 9 10

Duration: _____ **Final pulse:** _____

DATE	START	FINISH	DURATION

	SET 1	SET 2	SET 3	SET 4	SET 5	SET 6

Increase/Decrease Intensity

Training Log

DATE	START	FINISH	DURATION

Aerobic Activity:

Intensity level: 1 2 3 4 5 6 7 8 9 10

Duration: _____ **Final pulse:** _____

Increase/Decrease Intensity

	SET 1	SET 2	SET 3	SET 4	SET 5	SET 6
	@	@	@	@	@	@
	@	@	@	@	@	@
	@	@	@	@	@	@
	@	@	@	@	@	@
	@	@	@	@	@	@
	@	@	@	@	@	@
	@	@	@	@	@	@
	@	@	@	@	@	@
	@	@	@	@	@	@
	@	@	@	@	@	@

Aerobic Activity:

Intensity level: 1 2 3 4 5 6 7 8 9 10

Duration: _____ **Final pulse:** _____

DATE	START	FINISH	DURATION

	SET 1	SET 2	SET 3	SET 4	SET 5	SET 6
Increase/Decrease Intensity	@	@	@	@	@	@
	@	@	@	@	@	@
	@	@	@	@	@	@
	@	@	@	@	@	@
	@	@	@	@	@	@
	@	@	@	@	@	@
	@	@	@	@	@	@
	@	@	@	@	@	@
	@	@	@	@	@	@
	@	@	@	@	@	@
	@	@	@	@	@	@

Training Log

DATE	START	FINISH	DURATION

Aerobic Activity:

Intensity level: 1 2 3 4 5 6 7 8 9 10

Duration: _____ **Final pulse:** _____

	SET 1	SET 2	SET 3	SET 4	SET 5	SET 6
	@	@	@	@	@	@
	@	@	@	@	@	@
	@	@	@	@	@	@
	@	@	@	@	@	@
	@	@	@	@	@	@
	@	@	@	@	@	@
	@	@	@	@	@	@
	@	@	@	@	@	@
	@	@	@	@	@	@
	@	@	@	@	@	@

Increase/Decrease Intensity

Aerobic Activity:

Intensity level: 1 2 3 4 5 6 7 8 9 10

Duration: _____ **Final pulse:** _____

DATE	START	FINISH	DURATION

Increase/Decrease Intensity

SET 1	SET 2	SET 3	SET 4	SET 5	SET 6
@	@	@	@	@	@
@	@	@	@	@	@
@	@	@	@	@	@
@	@	@	@	@	@
@	@	@	@	@	@
@	@	@	@	@	@
@	@	@	@	@	@
@	@	@	@	@	@
@	@	@	@	@	@
@	@	@	@	@	@
@	@	@	@	@	@

233

Training Log

DATE	START	FINISH	DURATION

Aerobic Activity:

Intensity level: 1 2 3 4 5 6 7 8 9 10

Duration: _____ **Final pulse:** _____

	SET 1	SET 2	SET 3	SET 4	SET 5	SET 6

Increase/Decrease Intensity

@ @ @ @ @ @
@ @ @ @ @ @
@ @ @ @ @ @
@ @ @ @ @ @
@ @ @ @ @ @
@ @ @ @ @ @
@ @ @ @ @ @
@ @ @ @ @ @
@ @ @ @ @ @
@ @ @ @ @ @

Aerobic Activity:

Intensity level: *1 2 3 4 5 6 7 8 9 10*

Duration: _____ **Final pulse:** _____

DATE	START	FINISH	DURATION

	SET 1	SET 2	SET 3	SET 4	SET 5	SET 6
Increase/Decrease Intensity	@	@	@	@	@	@
	@	@	@	@	@	@
	@	@	@	@	@	@
	@	@	@	@	@	@
	@	@	@	@	@	@
	@	@	@	@	@	@
	@	@	@	@	@	@
	@	@	@	@	@	@
	@	@	@	@	@	@
	@	@	@	@	@	@

Training Log

DATE	START	FINISH	DURATION

Aerobic Activity:

Intensity level: 1 2 3 4 5 6 7 8 9 10

Duration: **Final pulse:**

	SET 1	SET 2	SET 3	SET 4	SET 5	SET 6
Increase/Decrease Intensity	@	@	@	@	@	@
	@	@	@	@	@	@
	@	@	@	@	@	@
	@	@	@	@	@	@
	@	@	@	@	@	@
	@	@	@	@	@	@
	@	@	@	@	@	@
	@	@	@	@	@	@
	@	@	@	@	@	@
	@	@	@	@	@	@

Aerobic Activity:

Intensity level: 1 2 3 4 5 6 7 8 9 10

Duration: _____ Final pulse: _____

DATE	START	FINISH	DURATION

	SET 1	SET 2	SET 3	SET 4	SET 5	SET 6

Increase/Decrease Intensity

Training Log

DATE	START	FINISH	DURATION

Increase/Decrease Intensity

SET 1　　SET 2　　SET 3　　SET 4　　SET 5　　SET 6

@ @ @ @ @ @
@ @ @ @ @ @
@ @ @ @ @ @
@ @ @ @ @ @
@ @ @ @ @ @
@ @ @ @ @ @
@ @ @ @ @ @
@ @ @ @ @ @
@ @ @ @ @ @
@ @ @ @ @ @

Aerobic Activity:

Intensity level: 1 2 3 4 5 6 7 8 9 10

Duration:　　*Final pulse:*

Aerobic Activity:

Intensity level: 1 2 3 4 5 6 7 8 9 10

Duration: **Final pulse:**

DATE	START	FINISH	DURATION

Increase/Decrease Intensity

SET 1　SET 2　SET 3　SET 4　SET 5　SET 6

Training Log

DATE	START	FINISH	DURATION

Aerobic Activity:

Intensity level: 1 2 3 4 5 6 7 8 9 10

Duration: _____ **Final pulse:** _____

	SET 1	SET 2	SET 3	SET 4	SET 5	SET 6
	@	@	@	@	@	@
	@	@	@	@	@	@
	@	@	@	@	@	@
	@	@	@	@	@	@
	@	@	@	@	@	@
	@	@	@	@	@	@
	@	@	@	@	@	@
	@	@	@	@	@	@
	@	@	@	@	@	@
	@	@	@	@	@	@
	@	@	@	@	@	@

Increase/Decrease Intensity

Aerobic Activity:

Intensity level: 1 2 3 4 5 6 7 8 9 10

Final pulse:

Duration:

DATE	START	FINISH	DURATION

	SET 1	SET 2	SET 3	SET 4	SET 5	SET 6
Increase/Decrease Intensity ▲ ▼	@	@	@	@	@	@
▲ ▼	@	@	@	@	@	@
▲ ▼	@	@	@	@	@	@
▲ ▼	@	@	@	@	@	@
▲ ▼	@	@	@	@	@	@
▲ ▼	@	@	@	@	@	@
▲ ▼	@	@	@	@	@	@
▲ ▼	@	@	@	@	@	@
▲ ▼	@	@	@	@	@	@
▲ ▼	@	@	@	@	@	@
▲ ▼	@	@	@	@	@	@

Training Log

DATE	START	FINISH	DURATION

Aerobic Activity:

Intensity level: 1 2 3 4 5 6 7 8 9 10

Duration:

Final pulse:

Increase/Decrease Intensity

SET 1   SET 2   SET 3   SET 4   SET 5   SET 6

@ @ @ @ @ @ @ @ @ @

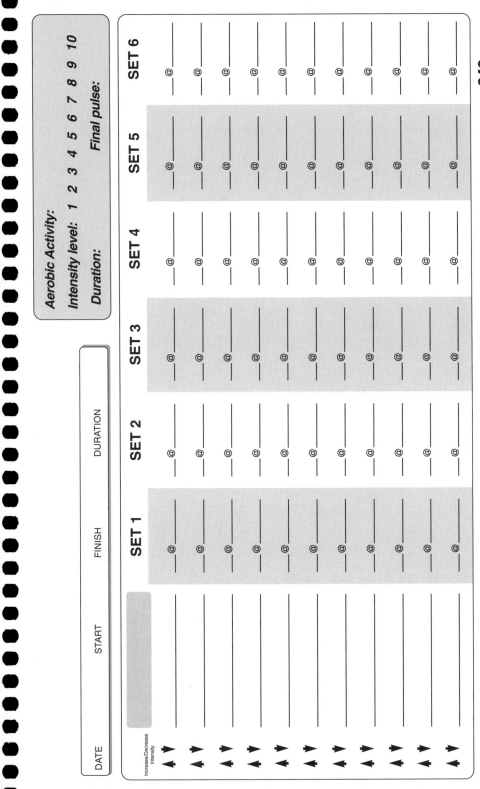

Training Log

DATE	START	FINISH	DURATION

Increase/Decrease Intensity

SET 1   SET 2   SET 3   SET 4   SET 5   SET 6

@   @   @   @   @   @

Aerobic Activity:

Intensity level: 1 2 3 4 5 6 7 8 9 10

Duration: *Final pulse:*

Aerobic Activity:

Intensity level: 1 2 3 4 5 6 7 8 9 10

Duration: _____ **Final pulse:** _____

DATE	START	FINISH	DURATION

Increase/Decrease Intensity

SET 1   SET 2   SET 3   SET 4   SET 5   SET 6

Training Log

DATE	START	FINISH	DURATION

Aerobic Activity:

Intensity level: 1 2 3 4 5 6 7 8 9 10

Duration: **Final pulse:**

Increase/Decrease Intensity

	SET 1	SET 2	SET 3	SET 4	SET 5	SET 6
	@	@	@	@	@	@
	@	@	@	@	@	@
	@	@	@	@	@	@
	@	@	@	@	@	@
	@	@	@	@	@	@
	@	@	@	@	@	@
	@	@	@	@	@	@
	@	@	@	@	@	@
	@	@	@	@	@	@
	@	@	@	@	@	@

Aerobic Activity:

Intensity level: 1 2 3 4 5 6 7 8 9 10

Duration: **Final pulse:**

DATE	START	FINISH	DURATION

Increase/Decrease Intensity

SET 1 | SET 2 | SET 3 | SET 4 | SET 5 | SET 6

@ @ @ @ @ @
@ @ @ @ @ @
@ @ @ @ @ @
@ @ @ @ @ @
@ @ @ @ @ @
@ @ @ @ @ @
@ @ @ @ @ @
@ @ @ @ @ @
@ @ @ @ @ @
@ @ @ @ @ @

EVALUATION
PAGE

DATE: _____ BODY WEIGHT: _____

STRENGTH

Exercises	LAST WORKOUT	FIRST W/O	GAIN
#1	_____ -	_____ =	_____
#2	_____ -	_____ =	_____
#3	_____ -	_____ =	_____
#4	_____ -	_____ =	_____
#5	_____ -	_____ =	_____
#6	_____ -	_____ =	_____
#7	_____ -	_____ =	_____
#8	_____ -	_____ =	_____

SIZE

SIZE	ACTUAL	GOAL	DIFFERENCE
NECK	_____ -	_____ =	_____
BICEPS	_____ -	_____ =	_____
FOREARMS	_____ -	_____ =	_____
CHEST	_____ -	_____ =	_____
WAIST	_____ -	_____ =	_____
HIPS	_____ -	_____ =	_____
THIGHS	_____ -	_____ =	_____
CALVES	_____ -	_____ =	_____
ANKLES	_____ -	_____ =	_____

248

How To Use The Nutrition Optimizer

The Nutrition Optimizer can accomodate up to 4 meals a day plus snacks

List quantity and type of food from *Foods List*

Total the carbs, proteins and fats from the meal

Record the specific proportions taken from *Foods List*

Use the calculation section to review your daily dietary intake

Compare your intake percentages to the recommended ones and adjust your diet accordingly

NUTRITION OPTIMIZER — DAY 1

MEAL 1	TIME 8:00 am	PROT	CARBS	FAT
300ml	Cornflakes	2	24	0
100ml	2% Milk	4	5	2
4 Slices	Wholewheat Toast	4	48	4
15ml	Margarine	0	0	11
250ml	Orange Juice	2	26	0
	TOTALS	16	103	17

MEAL 2	TIME 11:30 am	PROT	CARBS	FAT
4 Slices	Bread with butter	8	48	15
2 Slices	Ham	4	5	2
90 g	Cheese	4	48	4
123 g	Tomato	1	5	0
250ml	Tomato Juice	2	11	0
	TOTALS	41	64	49

MEAL 3	TIME 5:00 pm	PROT	CARBS	FAT
260 g	Steak	78	0	18
2	Baked Potato	10	104	0
30ml	Butter	0	0	22
250ml	Carrots, canned	2	17	0
200ml	Ice Cream	5	27	13
	TOTALS	95	148	53

250

MEAL 4	TIME	PROT	CARBS	FAT
	TOTALS			

SNACKS		PROT	CARBS	FAT
1	Banana	1	27	0
1	Brownie	1	10	6
250ml	Glass 2% Milk	9	12	5
	TOTALS	11	49	11

TOTAL GRAMS FROM ALL MEALS	163	364	130
	Box	Box	Box

STEP 1: CALCULATE TOTAL DAILY CALORIES

GRAMS OF PROTEIN	$\boxed{1}$ 163	x 4 =	$\boxed{4}$ 652
GRAMS OF CARBOHYDRATE	$\boxed{2}$ 364	x 4 =	$\boxed{5}$ 1456
GRAMS OF FAT	$\boxed{3}$ 130	x 9 =	$\boxed{6}$ 1170

Add boxes 4, 5, & 6

TOTAL DAILY CALORIES: $\boxed{7}$ 3278

STEP 2: CALCULATE PERCENTAGES OF NUTRIENTS

Your Percentages

CALORIES FROM PROTEIN	$\boxed{4}$ 652 ÷	$\boxed{7}$ 3278	x 100 =	$\boxed{8}$ 20 %
CALORIES FROM CARBS	$\boxed{5}$ 1456 ÷	$\boxed{7}$ 3278	x 100 =	$\boxed{9}$ 44 %
CALORIES FROM FAT	$\boxed{6}$ 1170 ÷	$\boxed{7}$ 3278	x 100 =	$\boxed{10}$ 35 %

STEP 3: COMPARE YOUR PERCENTAGES TO RECOMMENDED

RECOMMENDED PROTEIN	15%	vs	$\boxed{8}$ 20 %
RECOMMENDED CARBOHYDRATE	60-65%	vs	$\boxed{9}$ 44 %
RECOMMENDED FAT	20-25%	vs	$\boxed{10}$ 35 %

251

NUTRITION OPTIMIZER DAY 1

MEAL 1   TIME _____

	PROT	CARBS	FAT
TOTALS			

MEAL 2   TIME _____

	PROT	CARBS	FAT
TOTALS			

MEAL 3   TIME _____

	PROT	CARBS	FAT
TOTALS			

Meal 4

	Time _____	Prot	Carbs	Fat
		___	___	___
		___	___	___
		___	___	___
		___	___	___
		___	___	___
		___	___	___
		___	___	___
	Totals	___	___	___

Snacks

		Prot	Carbs	Fat
		___	___	___
		___	___	___
		___	___	___
		___	___	___
	Totals	___	___	___

Total Grams From All Meals

___ ___ ___
Box Box Box

Step 1: Calculate Total Daily Calories

GRAMS OF PROTEIN	[1]	x 4 =	[4]
GRAMS OF CARBOHYDRATE	[2]	x 4 =	[5]
GRAMS OF FAT	[3]	x 9 =	[6]

Add boxes 4, 5, & 6

TOTAL DAILY CALORIES: [7]

Step 2: Calculate Percentages of Nutrients

Your Percentages

CALORIES FROM PROTEIN	[4]	÷	[7]	x 100 =	[8] %
CALORIES FROM CARBS	[5]	÷	[7]	x 100 =	[9] %
CALORIES FROM FAT	[6]	÷	[7]	x 100 =	[10] %

Step 3: Compare Your Percentages to Recommended

Increase/Decrease Amount

RECOMMENDED PROTEIN	15%	vs	[8] %	↑ ↓
RECOMMENDED CARBOHYDRATE	60-65%	vs	[9] %	↑ ↓
RECOMMENDED FAT	20-25%	vs	[10] %	↑ ↓

NUTRITION OPTIMIZER DAY 2

MEAL 1   TIME _____   PROT CARBS FAT

_____   ____ ____ ____
_____   ____ ____ ____
_____   ____ ____ ____
_____   ____ ____ ____
_____   ____ ____ ____
_____   ____ ____ ____
_____   ____ ____ ____
                    TOTALS   ____ ____ ____

MEAL 2   TIME _____   PROT CARBS FAT

_____   ____ ____ ____
_____   ____ ____ ____
_____   ____ ____ ____
_____   ____ ____ ____
_____   ____ ____ ____
_____   ____ ____ ____
_____   ____ ____ ____
                    TOTALS   ____ ____ ____

MEAL 3   TIME _____   PROT CARBS FAT

_____   ____ ____ ____
_____   ____ ____ ____
_____   ____ ____ ____
_____   ____ ____ ____
_____   ____ ____ ____
_____   ____ ____ ____
_____   ____ ____ ____
                    TOTALS   ____ ____ ____

MEAL 4	TIME _____	PROT	CARBS	FAT
		___	___	___
		___	___	___
		___	___	___
		___	___	___
		___	___	___
		___	___	___
		___	___	___
	TOTALS	___	___	___

SNACKS		PROT	CARBS	FAT
		___	___	___
		___	___	___
		___	___	___
		___	___	___
		___	___	___
	TOTALS	___	___	___

TOTAL GRAMS FROM ALL MEALS   ___ ___ ___
                                  Box Box Box

STEP 1: CALCULATE TOTAL DAILY CALORIES

GRAMS OF PROTEIN [1]_____ x **4** = [4]_____

GRAMS OF CARBOHYDRATE [2]_____ x **4** = [5]_____

GRAMS OF FAT [3]_____ x **9** = [6]_____

Add boxes 4, 5, & 6

TOTAL DAILY CALORIES: [7]_____

STEP 2: CALCULATE PERCENTAGES OF NUTRIENTS

YOUR PERCENTAGES

CALORIES FROM PROTEIN [4]_____ ÷ [7]_____ x **100** = [8]_____ %

CALORIES FROM CARBS [5]_____ ÷ [7]_____ x **100** = [9]_____ %

CALORIES FROM FAT [6]_____ ÷ [7]_____ x **100** = [10]_____ %

STEP 3: COMPARE YOUR PERCENTAGES TO RECOMMENDED

Increase/Decrease Amount

RECOMMENDED PROTEIN **15%** VS [8]_____ % ▲ ▼

RECOMMENDED CARBOHYDRATE **60-65%** VS [9]_____ % ▲ ▼

RECOMMENDED FAT **20-25%** VS [10]_____ % ▲ ▼

253

NUTRITION OPTIMIZER

DAY 3

MEAL 1   TIME _____

	PROT	CARBS	FAT
TOTALS			

MEAL 2   TIME _____

	PROT	CARBS	FAT
TOTALS			

MEAL 3   TIME _____

	PROT	CARBS	FAT
TOTALS			

MEAL 4   TIME _____   PROT   CARBS   FAT

	PROT	CARBS	FAT
_____	___	___	___
_____	___	___	___
_____	___	___	___
_____	___	___	___
_____	___	___	___
_____	___	___	___
_____	___	___	___
TOTALS	___	___	___

SNACKS   PROT   CARBS   FAT

	PROT	CARBS	FAT
_____	___	___	___
_____	___	___	___
_____	___	___	___
_____	___	___	___
_____	___	___	___
TOTALS	___	___	___

TOTAL GRAMS FROM ALL MEALS   ___   ___   ___
                                      Box   Box   Box

STEP 1: CALCULATE TOTAL DAILY CALORIES

GRAMS OF PROTEIN   [1] _____ $x\,4 =$ [4] _____

GRAMS OF CARBOHYDRATE   [2] _____ $x\,4 =$ [5] _____

GRAMS OF FAT   [3] _____ $x\,9 =$ [6] _____

                               Add boxes 4, 5, & 6

TOTAL DAILY CALORIES: [7] _____

STEP 2: CALCULATE PERCENTAGES OF NUTRIENTS   YOUR PERCENTAGES

CALORIES FROM PROTEIN   [4] _____   ÷   [7] _____ $x\,100 =$ [8] _____ %

CALORIES FROM CARBS   [5] _____   ÷   [7] _____ $x\,100 =$ [9] _____ %

CALORIES FROM FAT   [6] _____   ÷   [7] _____ $x\,100 =$ [10] _____ %

STEP 3: COMPARE YOUR PERCENTAGES TO RECOMMENDED

                                                Increase/Decrease Amount

RECOMMENDED PROTEIN | 15% | VS   [8] ____ %   ↑ ↓

RECOMMENDED CARBOHYDRATE | 60-65% | VS   [9] ____ %   ↑ ↓

RECOMMENDED FAT | 20-25% | VS   [10] ____ %   ↑ ↓

NUTRITION OPTIMIZER   DAY 4

MEAL 1 TIME _____	PROT	CARBS	FAT
_____	____	____	____
_____	____	____	____
_____	____	____	____
_____	____	____	____
_____	____	____	____
_____	____	____	____
_____	____	____	____
_____	____	____	____
TOTALS	____	____	____

MEAL 2 TIME _____	PROT	CARBS	FAT
_____	____	____	____
_____	____	____	____
_____	____	____	____
_____	____	____	____
_____	____	____	____
_____	____	____	____
TOTALS	____	____	____

MEAL 3 TIME _____	PROT	CARBS	FAT
_____	____	____	____
_____	____	____	____
_____	____	____	____
_____	____	____	____
_____	____	____	____
_____	____	____	____
TOTALS	____	____	____

MEAL 4	TIME _____	PROT	CARBS	FAT
		___	___	___
		___	___	___
		___	___	___
		___	___	___
		___	___	___
		___	___	___
		___	___	___
	TOTALS	___	___	___

SNACKS		PROT	CARBS	FAT
		___	___	___
		___	___	___
		___	___	___
		___	___	___
	TOTALS	___	___	___

TOTAL GRAMS FROM ALL MEALS ___ ___ ___
Box   Box   Box

STEP 1: CALCULATE TOTAL DAILY CALORIES

GRAMS OF PROTEIN [1] ____ x **4** = [4] ____

GRAMS OF CARBOHYDRATE [2] ____ x **4** = [5] ____

GRAMS OF FAT [3] ____ x **9** = [6] ____

Add boxes 4, 5, & 6

TOTAL DAILY CALORIES: [7] ____

STEP 2: CALCULATE PERCENTAGES OF NUTRIENTS

YOUR PERCENTAGES

CALORIES FROM PROTEIN [4] ____ ÷ [7] ____ x **100** = [8] ____ %

CALORIES FROM CARBS [5] ____ ÷ [7] ____ x **100** = [9] ____ %

CALORIES FROM FAT [6] ____ ÷ [7] ____ x **100** = [10] ____ %

STEP 3: COMPARE YOUR PERCENTAGES TO RECOMMENDED

Increase/Decrease Amount

RECOMMENDED PROTEIN | 15% | VS | [8] ____ % | ▲ ▼

RECOMMENDED CARBOHYDRATE | 60-65% | VS | [9] ____ % | ▲ ▼

RECOMMENDED FAT | 20-25% | VS | [10] ____ % | ▲ ▼

NUTRITION OPTIMIZER

DAY 5

MEAL 1 TIME _____	PROT	CARBS	FAT
_____	___	___	___
_____	___	___	___
_____	___	___	___
_____	___	___	___
_____	___	___	___
_____	___	___	___
_____	___	___	___
TOTALS	___	___	___

MEAL 2 TIME _____	PROT	CARBS	FAT
_____	___	___	___
_____	___	___	___
_____	___	___	___
_____	___	___	___
_____	___	___	___
_____	___	___	___
_____	___	___	___
TOTALS	___	___	___

MEAL 3 TIME _____	PROT	CARBS	FAT
_____	___	___	___
_____	___	___	___
_____	___	___	___
_____	___	___	___
_____	___	___	___
_____	___	___	___
_____	___	___	___
TOTALS	___	___	___

MEAL 4   TIME _____

	PROT	CARBS	FAT
TOTALS	____	____	____

SNACKS

	PROT	CARBS	FAT
TOTALS	____	____	____

TOTAL GRAMS FROM ALL MEALS

____ ____ ____
Box   Box   Box

STEP 1: CALCULATE TOTAL DAILY CALORIES

GRAMS OF PROTEIN [1] □ x **4** = [4] □

GRAMS OF CARBOHYDRATE [2] □ x **4** = [5] □

GRAMS OF FAT [3] □ x **9** = [6] □

Add boxes 4, 5, & 6

TOTAL DAILY CALORIES: [7] □ ←

STEP 2: CALCULATE PERCENTAGES OF NUTRIENTS

YOUR PERCENTAGES

CALORIES FROM PROTEIN [4] □ ÷ [7] □ x **100** = [8] □ %

CALORIES FROM CARBS [5] □ ÷ [7] □ x **100** = [9] □ %

CALORIES FROM FAT [6] □ ÷ [7] □ x **100** = [10] □ %

STEP 3: COMPARE YOUR PERCENTAGES TO RECOMMENDED

Increase/Decrease Amount

RECOMMENDED PROTEIN | **15%** | VS | [8] □ % | ▲ ▼

RECOMMENDED CARBOHYDRATE | **60-65%** | VS | [9] □ % | ▲ ▼

RECOMMENDED FAT | **20-25%** | VS | [10] □ % | ▲ ▼

NUTRITION OPTIMIZER

DAY 6

MEAL 1	TIME _____	PROT	CARBS	FAT
	TOTALS			

MEAL 2	TIME _____	PROT	CARBS	FAT
	TOTALS			

MEAL 3	TIME _____	PROT	CARBS	FAT
	TOTALS			

MEAL 4   TIME _____

	PROT	CARBS	FAT
_____	___	___	___
_____	___	___	___
_____	___	___	___
_____	___	___	___
_____	___	___	___
_____	___	___	___
TOTALS	___	___	___

SNACKS

	PROT	CARBS	FAT
_____	___	___	___
_____	___	___	___
_____	___	___	___
_____	___	___	___
TOTALS	___	___	___

TOTAL GRAMS FROM ALL MEALS   ___   ___   ___
Box   Box   Box

STEP 1: CALCULATE TOTAL DAILY CALORIES

GRAMS OF PROTEIN [1] _____ x 4 = [4] _____

GRAMS OF CARBOHYDRATE [2] _____ x 4 = [5] _____

GRAMS OF FAT [3] _____ x 9 = [6] _____

Add boxes 4, 5, & 6

TOTAL DAILY CALORIES: [7] _____

STEP 2: CALCULATE PERCENTAGES OF NUTRIENTS   YOUR PERCENTAGES

CALORIES FROM PROTEIN [4] _____ ÷ [7] _____ x **100** = [8] ___ %

CALORIES FROM CARBS [5] _____ ÷ [7] _____ x **100** = [9] ___ %

CALORIES FROM FAT [6] _____ ÷ [7] _____ x **100** = [10] ___ %

STEP 3: COMPARE YOUR PERCENTAGES TO RECOMMENDED

Increase/Decrease Amount

RECOMMENDED PROTEIN	15%	VS	[8] ___ % ▲ ▼
RECOMMENDED CARBOHYDRATE	60-65%	VS	[9] ___ % ▲ ▼
RECOMMENDED FAT	20-25%	VS	[10] ___ % ▲ ▼

261

NUTRITION OPTIMIZER DAY 7

MEAL 1   TIME _____   PROT   CARBS   FAT

_____   ____   ____   ____
_____   ____   ____   ____
_____   ____   ____   ____
_____   ____   ____   ____
_____   ____   ____   ____
_____   ____   ____   ____
_____   ____   ____   ____
                    TOTALS   ____   ____   ____

MEAL 2   TIME _____   PROT   CARBS   FAT

_____   ____   ____   ____
_____   ____   ____   ____
_____   ____   ____   ____
_____   ____   ____   ____
_____   ____   ____   ____
_____   ____   ____   ____
_____   ____   ____   ____
                    TOTALS   ____   ____   ____

MEAL 3   TIME _____   PROT   CARBS   FAT

_____   ____   ____   ____
_____   ____   ____   ____
_____   ____   ____   ____
_____   ____   ____   ____
_____   ____   ____   ____
_____   ____   ____   ____
_____   ____   ____   ____
                    TOTALS   ____   ____   ____

MEAL 4   TIME _____   PROT CARBS FAT

	PROT	CARBS	FAT
_____	____	____	____
_____	____	____	____
_____	____	____	____
_____	____	____	____
_____	____	____	____
_____	____	____	____
_____	____	____	____
TOTALS	____	____	____

SNACKS   PROT CARBS FAT

	PROT	CARBS	FAT
_____	____	____	____
_____	____	____	____
_____	____	____	____
_____	____	____	____
_____	____	____	____
TOTALS	____	____	____

TOTAL GRAMS FROM ALL MEALS   ____   ____   ____
                                        Box   Box   Box

STEP 1: CALCULATE TOTAL DAILY CALORIES

GRAMS OF PROTEIN   [1] _____   x **4** =   [4] _____

GRAMS OF CARBOHYDRATE   [2] _____   x **4** =   [5] _____   Add boxes
                                                                        4, 5, & 6
GRAMS OF FAT   [3] _____   x **9** =   [6] _____

TOTAL DAILY CALORIES: [7] _____ ←

STEP 2: CALCULATE PERCENTAGES OF NUTRIENTS   YOUR PERCENTAGES

CALORIES FROM PROTEIN   [4] _____ ÷ [7] _____ x **100** = [8] _____ %

CALORIES FROM CARBS   [5] _____ ÷ [7] _____ x **100** = [9] _____ %

CALORIES FROM FAT   [6] _____ ÷ [7] _____ x **100** = [10] _____ %

STEP 3: COMPARE YOUR PERCENTAGES TO RECOMMENDED

				Increase/Decrease Amount
RECOMMENDED PROTEIN	**15%**	VS	[8] _____ %	▲ ▼
RECOMMENDED CARBOHYDRATE	**60-65%**	VS	[9] _____ %	▲ ▼
RECOMMENDED FAT	**20-25%**	VS	[10] _____ %	▲ ▼

263

NUTRITION OPTIMIZER — DAY 8

MEAL 1　TIME _____

	PROT	CARBS	FAT
TOTALS			

MEAL 2　TIME _____

	PROT	CARBS	FAT
TOTALS			

MEAL 3　TIME _____

	PROT	CARBS	FAT
TOTALS			

MEAL 4   TIME _____   PROT CARBS FAT

	PROT	CARBS	FAT
	___	___	___
	___	___	___
	___	___	___
	___	___	___
	___	___	___
	___	___	___
	___	___	___
TOTALS	___	___	___

SNACKS   PROT CARBS FAT

	PROT	CARBS	FAT
	___	___	___
	___	___	___
	___	___	___
	___	___	___
	___	___	___
TOTALS	___	___	___

TOTAL GRAMS FROM ALL MEALS
___	___	___
Box	Box	Box

STEP 1: CALCULATE TOTAL DAILY CALORIES

GRAMS OF PROTEIN [1] [____] x **4** = [4] [____]

GRAMS OF CARBOHYDRATE [2] [____] x **4** = [5] [____]   Add boxes 4, 5, & 6

GRAMS OF FAT [3] [____] x **9** = [6] [____]

TOTAL DAILY CALORIES: [7] [____] ←

STEP 2: CALCULATE PERCENTAGES OF NUTRIENTS   YOUR PERCENTAGES

CALORIES FROM PROTEIN [4] [____] ÷ [7] [____] x **100** = [8] [____] %

CALORIES FROM CARBS [5] [____] ÷ [7] [____] x **100** = [9] [____] %

CALORIES FROM FAT [6] [____] ÷ [7] [____] x **100** = [10] [____] %

STEP 3: COMPARE YOUR PERCENTAGES TO RECOMMENDED

Increase/Decrease Amount

RECOMMENDED PROTEIN   **15%**   VS   [8] [____] %   ▲ ▼

RECOMMENDED CARBOHYDRATE   **60-65%**   VS   [9] [____] %   ▲ ▼

RECOMMENDED FAT   **20-25%**   VS   [10] [____] %   ▲ ▼

NUTRITION OPTIMIZER

DAY 9

MEAL 1   TIME _____   PROT   CARBS   FAT

	PROT	CARBS	FAT
TOTALS			

MEAL 2   TIME _____   PROT   CARBS   FAT

	PROT	CARBS	FAT
TOTALS			

MEAL 3   TIME _____   PROT   CARBS   FAT

	PROT	CARBS	FAT
TOTALS			

Meal 4

	Time _____	Prot	Carbs	Fat
		____	____	____
		____	____	____
		____	____	____
		____	____	____
		____	____	____
		____	____	____
		____	____	____
	Totals	____	____	____

Snacks

		Prot	Carbs	Fat
		____	____	____
		____	____	____
		____	____	____
		____	____	____
	Totals	____	____	____

Total Grams From All Meals

____ ____ ____
Box Box Box

STEP 1: Calculate Total Daily Calories

GRAMS OF PROTEIN [1] [____] x **4** = [4] [____]

GRAMS OF CARBOHYDRATE [2] [____] x **4** = [5] [____]

GRAMS OF FAT [3] [____] x **9** = [6] [____]

Add boxes 4, 5, & 6

TOTAL DAILY CALORIES: [7] [____]

STEP 2: Calculate Percentages of Nutrients

YOUR PERCENTAGES

CALORIES FROM PROTEIN [4] [____] ÷ [7] [____] x **100** = [8] [____] %

CALORIES FROM CARBS [5] [____] ÷ [7] [____] x **100** = [9] [____] %

CALORIES FROM FAT [6] [____] ÷ [7] [____] x **100** = [10] [____] %

STEP 3: Compare Your Percentages to Recommended

Increase/Decrease Amount

RECOMMENDED PROTEIN	15%	VS	[8] ____ % ▲ ▼
RECOMMENDED CARBOHYDRATE	60-65%	VS	[9] ____ % ▲ ▼
RECOMMENDED FAT	20-25%	VS	[10] ____ % ▲ ▼

NUTRITION OPTIMIZER   DAY 10

MEAL 1   TIME _____   PROT CARBS FAT

_____	___	___	___
_____	___	___	___
_____	___	___	___
_____	___	___	___
_____	___	___	___
_____	___	___	___
_____	___	___	___
TOTALS	___	___	___

MEAL 2   TIME _____   PROT CARBS FAT

_____	___	___	___
_____	___	___	___
_____	___	___	___
_____	___	___	___
_____	___	___	___
_____	___	___	___
_____	___	___	___
TOTALS	___	___	___

MEAL 3   TIME _____   PROT CARBS FAT

_____	___	___	___
_____	___	___	___
_____	___	___	___
_____	___	___	___
_____	___	___	___
_____	___	___	___
_____	___	___	___
TOTALS	___	___	___

MEAL 4 TIME _____

	PROT	CARBS	FAT
_____	____	____	____
_____	____	____	____
_____	____	____	____
_____	____	____	____
_____	____	____	____
_____	____	____	____
_____	____	____	____
TOTALS	____	____	____

SNACKS

	PROT	CARBS	FAT
_____	____	____	____
_____	____	____	____
_____	____	____	____
_____	____	____	____
TOTALS	____	____	____

TOTAL GRAMS FROM ALL MEALS

____ ____ ____
Box Box Box

STEP 1: CALCULATE TOTAL DAILY CALORIES

GRAMS OF PROTEIN [1] $\times 4 =$ [4]

GRAMS OF CARBOHYDRATE [2] $\times 4 =$ [5]

GRAMS OF FAT [3] $\times 9 =$ [6]

Add boxes 4, 5, & 6

TOTAL DAILY CALORIES: [7]

STEP 2: CALCULATE PERCENTAGES OF NUTRIENTS

YOUR PERCENTAGES

CALORIES FROM PROTEIN [4] $\div$ [7] $\times 100 =$ [8] %

CALORIES FROM CARBS [5] $\div$ [7] $\times 100 =$ [9] %

CALORIES FROM FAT [6] $\div$ [7] $\times 100 =$ [10] %

STEP 3: COMPARE YOUR PERCENTAGES TO RECOMMENDED

Increase/Decrease Amount

RECOMMENDED PROTEIN	15%	VS	[8] %	▲ ▼
RECOMMENDED CARBOHYDRATE	60-65%	VS	[9] %	▲ ▼
RECOMMENDED FAT	20-25%	VS	[10] %	▲ ▼

NUTRITION OPTIMIZER

DAY 11

MEAL 1   TIME _____

	PROT	CARBS	FAT
TOTALS			

MEAL 2   TIME _____

	PROT	CARBS	FAT
TOTALS			

MEAL 3   TIME _____

	PROT	CARBS	FAT
TOTALS			

MEAL 4

		PROT	CARBS	FAT
TIME _____				
_____		___	___	___
_____		___	___	___
_____		___	___	___
_____		___	___	___
_____		___	___	___
_____		___	___	___
_____		___	___	___
TOTALS		___	___	___

SNACKS

	PROT	CARBS	FAT
_____	___	___	___
_____	___	___	___
_____	___	___	___
_____	___	___	___
_____	___	___	___
TOTALS	___	___	___

TOTAL GRAMS FROM ALL MEALS

___ ___ ___
Box Box Box

STEP 1: CALCULATE TOTAL DAILY CALORIES

GRAMS OF PROTEIN [1] □ $\times 4 =$ [4] □

GRAMS OF CARBOHYDRATE [2] □ $\times 4 =$ [5] □

GRAMS OF FAT [3] □ $\times 9 =$ [6] □

Add boxes 4, 5, & 6

TOTAL DAILY CALORIES: [7] □

STEP 2: CALCULATE PERCENTAGES OF NUTRIENTS

YOUR PERCENTAGES

CALORIES FROM PROTEIN [4] □ $\div$ [7] □ $\times 100 =$ [8] □ %

CALORIES FROM CARBS [5] □ $\div$ [7] □ $\times 100 =$ [9] □ %

CALORIES FROM FAT [6] □ $\div$ [7] □ $\times 100 =$ [10] □ %

STEP 3: COMPARE YOUR PERCENTAGES TO RECOMMENDED

Increase/Decrease Amount

RECOMMENDED PROTEIN | 15% | VS | [8] □ % | ▲ ▼

RECOMMENDED CARBOHYDRATE | 60-65% | VS | [9] □ % | ▲ ▼

RECOMMENDED FAT | 20-25% | VS | [10] □ % | ▲ ▼

271

NUTRITION OPTIMIZER

DAY 12

MEAL 1   TIME _____   **PROT   CARBS   FAT**

_____   ____   ____   ____
_____   ____   ____   ____
_____   ____   ____   ____
_____   ____   ____   ____
_____   ____   ____   ____
_____   ____   ____   ____
_____   ____   ____   ____

                 TOTALS   ____   ____   ____

MEAL 2   TIME _____   **PROT   CARBS   FAT**

_____   ____   ____   ____
_____   ____   ____   ____
_____   ____   ____   ____
_____   ____   ____   ____
_____   ____   ____   ____
_____   ____   ____   ____
_____   ____   ____   ____

                 TOTALS   ____   ____   ____

MEAL 3   TIME _____   **PROT   CARBS   FAT**

_____   ____   ____   ____
_____   ____   ____   ____
_____   ____   ____   ____
_____   ____   ____   ____
_____   ____   ____   ____
_____   ____   ____   ____
_____   ____   ____   ____

                 TOTALS   ____   ____   ____

MEAL 4   TIME _____

	PROT	CARBS	FAT
_____	___	___	___
_____	___	___	___
_____	___	___	___
_____	___	___	___
_____	___	___	___
_____	___	___	___
_____	___	___	___
TOTALS	___	___	___

SNACKS

	PROT	CARBS	FAT
_____	___	___	___
_____	___	___	___
_____	___	___	___
_____	___	___	___
_____	___	___	___
TOTALS	___	___	___

TOTAL GRAMS FROM ALL MEALS

___ ___ ___
Box Box Box

STEP 1: CALCULATE TOTAL DAILY CALORIES

GRAMS OF PROTEIN [1] $\times 4 =$ [4]

GRAMS OF CARBOHYDRATE [2] $\times 4 =$ [5]

GRAMS OF FAT [3] $\times 9 =$ [6]

Add boxes 4, 5, & 6

TOTAL DAILY CALORIES: [7]

STEP 2: CALCULATE PERCENTAGES OF NUTRIENTS

YOUR PERCENTAGES

CALORIES FROM PROTEIN [4] $\div$ [7] $\times 100 =$ [8] %

CALORIES FROM CARBS [5] $\div$ [7] $\times 100 =$ [9] %

CALORIES FROM FAT [6] $\div$ [7] $\times 100 =$ [10] %

STEP 3: COMPARE YOUR PERCENTAGES TO RECOMMENDED

Increase/Decrease Amount

RECOMMENDED PROTEIN	15%	VS	[8] %	▲ ▼
RECOMMENDED CARBOHYDRATE	60-65%	VS	[9] %	▲ ▼
RECOMMENDED FAT	20-25%	VS	[10] %	▲ ▼

273

NUTRITION OPTIMIZER

DAY 13

MEAL 1   TIME _____

	PROT	CARBS	FAT
TOTALS			

MEAL 2   TIME _____

	PROT	CARBS	FAT
TOTALS			

MEAL 3   TIME _____

	PROT	CARBS	FAT
TOTALS			

MEAL 4

TIME _____

	PROT	CARBS	FAT
_____	___	___	___
_____	___	___	___
_____	___	___	___
_____	___	___	___
_____	___	___	___
_____	___	___	___
_____	___	___	___
TOTALS	___	___	___

SNACKS

	PROT	CARBS	FAT
_____	___	___	___
_____	___	___	___
_____	___	___	___
_____	___	___	___
_____	___	___	___
TOTALS	___	___	___

TOTAL GRAMS FROM ALL MEALS

___ ___ ___
Box   Box   Box

STEP 1: CALCULATE TOTAL DAILY CALORIES

GRAMS OF PROTEIN ⬚[1] $\times 4 =$ ⬚[4]

GRAMS OF CARBOHYDRATE ⬚[2] $\times 4 =$ ⬚[5]

GRAMS OF FAT ⬚[3] $\times 9 =$ ⬚[6]

Add boxes 4, 5, & 6

TOTAL DAILY CALORIES: ⬚[7]

STEP 2: CALCULATE PERCENTAGES OF NUTRIENTS

YOUR PERCENTAGES

CALORIES FROM PROTEIN ⬚[4] $\div$ ⬚[7] $\times 100 =$ ⬚[8] %

CALORIES FROM CARBS ⬚[5] $\div$ ⬚[7] $\times 100 =$ ⬚[9] %

CALORIES FROM FAT ⬚[6] $\div$ ⬚[7] $\times 100 =$ ⬚[10] %

STEP 3: COMPARE YOUR PERCENTAGES TO RECOMMENDED

Increase/Decrease Amount

RECOMMENDED PROTEIN	15%	VS	[8] % ▲ ▼
RECOMMENDED CARBOHYDRATE	60-65%	VS	[9] % ▲ ▼
RECOMMENDED FAT	20-25%	VS	[10] % ▲ ▼

275

NUTRITION OPTIMIZER

DAY 14

MEAL 1   TIME _____   PROT CARBS FAT

	PROT	CARBS	FAT
TOTALS			

MEAL 2   TIME _____   PROT CARBS FAT

	PROT	CARBS	FAT
TOTALS			

MEAL 3   TIME _____   PROT CARBS FAT

	PROT	CARBS	FAT
TOTALS			

MEAL 4   TIME _____

	PROT	CARBS	FAT
	____	____	____
	____	____	____
	____	____	____
	____	____	____
	____	____	____
	____	____	____
	____	____	____
TOTALS	____	____	____

SNACKS

	PROT	CARBS	FAT
	____	____	____
	____	____	____
	____	____	____
	____	____	____
	____	____	____
TOTALS	____	____	____

TOTAL GRAMS FROM ALL MEALS

____ ____ ____
Box   Box   Box

STEP 1: CALCULATE TOTAL DAILY CALORIES

GRAMS OF PROTEIN [1] ☐ x **4** = [4] ☐

GRAMS OF CARBOHYDRATE [2] ☐ x **4** = [5] ☐

GRAMS OF FAT [3] ☐ x **9** = [6] ☐

Add boxes 4, 5, & 6

TOTAL DAILY CALORIES: [7] ☐

STEP 2: CALCULATE PERCENTAGES OF NUTRIENTS

YOUR PERCENTAGES

CALORIES FROM PROTEIN [4] ÷ [7] x **100** = [8] ____ %

CALORIES FROM CARBS [5] ÷ [7] x **100** = [9] ____ %

CALORIES FROM FAT [6] ÷ [7] x **100** = [10] ____ %

STEP 3: COMPARE YOUR PERCENTAGES TO RECOMMENDED

Increase/Decrease Amount

RECOMMENDED PROTEIN	15%	VS	[8] ____ %	▲ ▼
RECOMMENDED CARBOHYDRATE	60-65%	VS	[9] ____ %	▲ ▼
RECOMMENDED FAT	20-25%	VS	[10] ____ %	▲ ▼

277

FOODS LIST

MEASURE	WEIGHT (g)	FOOD ENERGY (cal)	PROTEIN (g)	CARBOHYDRATE (g)	FAT (g)

DAIRY PRODUCTS
Milk

	MEASURE	WEIGHT (g)	FOOD ENERGY (cal)	PROTEIN (g)	CARBOHYDRATE (g)	FAT (g)
Butter Milk	250 ml	259	105	9	12	2
Whole Milk, 3.3% B.F.	250 ml	258	159	8	12	9
Partly Skimmed, 2% B.F.	250 ml	258	128	9	12	5
Skim	250 ml	259	90	9	13	tr
Chocolate, 2% B.F.	250 ml	264	189	8	27	5
Milk shake, chocolate	250 ml	211	250	6	45	6
Milk shake, vanilla	250 ml	207	231	8	37	6
Egg Nog	250 ml	268	361	10	36	20
Cheese						
Blue	N/A	45	159	10	1	13
Brick	N/A	45	167	10	1	13
Camembert	N/A	45	135	9	tr	11
Cheddar	N/A	45	181	11	tr	15
Cottage, 2% B.F.	250 ml	239	214	33	9	5
Cream	15 ml	15	52	1	tr	5
Feta	N/A	45	123	7	2	10
Mozzarella	N/A	45	132	9	1	10
Mozzarella, partly skimmed	N/A	45	118	11	1	7
Parmesan, grated	15 ml	5	23	2	tr	2
Processed, cheddar	N/A	45	169	10	tr	14
Processed, spread, cheddar	15 ml	15	44	2	1	3
Ricotta, made with whole milk	N/A	45	78	5	1	6
Swiss	N/A	45	169	13	2	12
Cream						
Cereal, 1/2 & 1/2, 12% B.F.	15 ml	15	20	tr	tr	2
Sour, 14% B.F.	15 ml	15	23	tr	tr	2
Table (coffee), 18% B.F.	15 ml	15	28	tr	tr	3
Whipping, 35% B.F.	15 ml	15	49	tr	tr	5
Whipping, pressurized	15 ml	4	10	tr	tr	tr
Yogurt						
Coffee and vanilla varieties, 1.25 %B.F.	N/A	125	107	6	17	2
Frozen, fruit, 6.3% B.F.	N/A	125	148	4	23	5
Fruit flavour, 1.4% B.F.	N/A	125	131	6	23	2
Plain, 1.5% B.F.	N/A	125	79	7	9	2
Desserts						
Ice cream, van., 10% B.F.	125 ml	70	142	3	17	8
Ice milk, vanilla, soft	125 ml	92	129	4	20	4
Pudding, can, chocolate	125 ml	132	191	3	28	10
Pudding, rice with raisins	125 ml	140	204	5	37	4
Sherbet, orange	125 ml	102	143	1	31	2

FOODS LIST

	Measure	Weight (g)	Food Energy (cal)	Protein (g)	Carbohydrate (g)	Fat (g)
EGGS, LARGE						
Egg, fried in butter	1 egg	46	83	5	tr	6
Egg, white, raw	1 white	33	16	3	tr	tr
Egg, yolk, raw	1 yolk	17	63	3	tr	6
Egg substitute	60 ml	61	97	7	2	7
MEAT, FISH, POULTRY AND RELATED PRODUCTS						
Assorted meat products						
Blood sausage (12cm x 0.2cm)	1 slice	30	113	4	tr	10
Bologna, beef and pork (11cm x 0.2cm)	1 slice	22	70	3	tr	6
Creton	15 ml	13	59	2	tr	5
Ham, luncheon meat, sliced, packaged, (1cm x 1cm x 0.2cm)	1 slice	27	49	5	tr	3
Liverwurst	15 ml	15	49	2	tr	4
Salami, cooked, beef and pork, (11cm diam x 0.2cm)	1 slice	22	55	3	tr	4
Salami, dry type (4.5cm diam x 0.3cm)	1 slice	6	25	1	tr	2
Sausage, beef & pork 16 per 500g package	1 sausage	15	59	2	tr	5
Wieners, beef & pork, 12 per 450g package	1 wiener	37	118	4	tr	11
Wieners, chicken, 12 per 450 g package	1 wiener	37	95	5	3	7
Beef						
Corned, brisket, cooked	N/A	90	226	16	tr	17
Ground, lean, broiled (8cm diam x 1.5cm) med	1 patty	88	209	22	0	13
Ground, reg, broiled						
(8cm diam x 1.5cm) med	1 patty	88	254	21	0	18
(8cm diam x 1.5cm) well done	1 patty	88	257	24	0	17
Ground, reg., pan-fried						
(8cm diam. x 1.5cm) med	1 patty	88	269	21	0	20
(8cm diam. x 1.5cm) well done	1 patty	88	252	24	0	17
Roast rib, roasted, (11cm x 6cm x 0.6cm) lean and fat	2 pieces	89	256	22	0	18
Steak, inside, round, broiled (11cm x 6cm x 1.2cm) lean and fat	1 piece	88	154	26	0	5
Steak, sirloin, broiled, lean (11cm x 6cm x 1.2cm)	1 piece	88	163	26	0	6
Stewing, simmered, lean	250 ml	148	335	49	0	14
Fish						
Boston blue fish, baked or broiled (12cm x 7cm x 1cm)	1 piece	92	146	24	0	5

FOODS LIST

	Measure	Weight (g)	Food Energy (cal)	Protein (g)	Carbohydrate (g)	Fat (g)
Cod, fresh, broiled with butter (10cm x 4cm x 2cm)	1 piece	88	150	25	0	5
Fish sticks, breaded	3 sticks	90	158	15	6	8
Haddock, bread crumb milk and egg, coated and fried	1 fillet	110	182	22	6	7
Herring, smoked, kippered (11cm x 4cm x 0.6cm)	1 fillet	55	116	12	0	7
Shrimp, canned, solids	28 med.	90	104	22	tr	tr
Sole, baked with butter	1 fillet	90	127	17	tr	6
Trout, lake, broiled or baked (17cm x 5cm x 1cm)	1 piece	93	201	21	tr	13
Tuna, canned in oil	125 ml	85	167	24	0	7
Tuna, canned in water	125 ml	85	135	30	0	1
Lamb						
Leg, roasted, lean (11cm x 6cm x 0.6cm)	2 slices	87	243	22	0	16
Loin chop, broiled, lean	1 chop	87	164	25	0	7
Shoulder, roasted, lean (7cm x 6cm x 0.6cm)	3 slices	83	170	22	0	8
Organ and Glandular Meats						
Heart, beef, simmered	150 ml	92	161	26	tr	5
Kidney, beef, simmered	150 ml	89	128	23	tr	3
Liver, beef, pan-fried (16cm x 6cm x 1cm)	1 piece	86	187	23	7	7
Liver, chicken, simmered	5 livers	100	157	24	tr	5
Pork, Cured and Fresh						
Bacon, back, grilled	1 slice	23	43	6	tr	2
Bacon, side pan-fried	2 slices	13	75	4	tr	6
Ham, roasted, (11cm x 6cm x 0.6cm) lean and fat	2 slices	87	211	19	0	15
Loin, centre cut chop, broiled, lean	1 chop	72	159	23	0	7
Spareribs, lean & fat	2 med.	70	235	18	0	18
Tenderloin, roasted, lean (4cm x 4cm x 1.5cm)	3 slices	89	148	26	0	4
Poultry						
Chicken, broiler, roasted breast, meat only	1/2 brst	86	142	27	0	3
breast, meat plus skin	1/2 brst	98	193	29	0	8
drumstick, meat only	2	88	151	25	0	5
Chicken, roasted, flesh only (7cm x 5cm x 0.6cm)	4 slices	92	154	23	0	6
Turkey, all classes, roasted						

280

FOODS LIST

	Measure	Weight (g)	Food Energy (cal)	Protein (g)	Carbohydrate (g)	Fat (g)
dark meat only	2 slices	86	161	25	0	6
light meat only	2 slices	86	135	26	0	3
Veal						
Loin, cutlet or chop, broiled						
(7cm x 6cm x 2cm)	1 piece	92	215	24	0	12
Round with rump, broiled						
(11cm x 6cm x 0.6cm)	2 slices	87	188	24	0	10
LENTILS, NUTS, AND SEEDS						
Almonds, shelled, whole	125 ml	75	442	15	15	39
Cashew nuts, roasted	125 ml	69	397	11	20	33
Chic peas, Garbanzos, boiled, drained	250 ml	173	284	15	47	4
Coconut, dried, sweetened	125 ml	49	245	1	23	17
Lentils, cooked, drained	250 ml	209	243	19	42	1
Lima, cooked, drained	250 ml	199	228	15	41	1
Nuts, mixed, dry roasted						
with peanuts	125 ml	72	428	12	18	37
Peanut butter	15 ml	16	95	5	3	8
Peanuts, oil roasted	125 ml	77	447	21	14	38
Pistachio nuts, dry roasted	125 ml	68	412	10	19	36
Red kidney cooked drained	250 ml	187	238	16	43	1
Soybeans, mature seeds,						
cooked, drained	250 ml	182	314	30	18	16
Tofu (7cm x 6cm x 2cm)	1 piece	89	68	7	2	4
Walnuts, English, chopped	15 ml	6	39	tr	1	4
VEGETABLES, RELATED PRODUCTS						
Asparagus, boiled	250 ml	190	48	5	8	tr
Asparagus, canned	250 ml	256	49	5	6	2
Bean sprouts, stir-fried	250 ml	131	66	6	14	tr
Beans, snap green, yellow,						
or Italian, boiled,	250 ml	132	46	2	10	tr
canned, drained	250 ml	144	29	2	6	tr
Beets, canned, drained	250 ml	180	56	2	13	tr
Broccoli, spears, boiled	250 ml	164	48	5	9	tr
Broccoli, raw, med sized	1 spear	151	42	5	8	tr
Brussels sprouts, boiled	250 ml	165	64	4	14	tr
Cabbage, shredded, boiled	250 ml	158	33	2	8	tr
Cabbage, shredded, raw	250 ml	74	18	tr	4	tr
Carrots, boiled, drained	250 ml	165	74	2	17	tr
Carrots, raw, 19cm long	1	72	31	tr	7	tr
Cauliflower, boiled	250 ml	131	31	2	6	tr
Celery, raw, 19cm long	1 stalk	40	6	tr	1	tr

281

FOODS LIST

	Measure	Weight (g)	Food Energy (cal)	Protein (g)	Carbohydrate (g)	Fat (g)
Corn, canned, cream style	250 ml	270	194	5	49	1
Corn, canned, kernels	250 ml	173	140	5	32	2
Cucumber, raw, sliced	250 ml	111	14	tr	3	tr
Eggplant, cubed, boiled, drained	250 ml	101	28	tr	7	tr
Lettuce, iceberg, raw	1 leaf	20	3	tr	tr	tr
Mushrooms, boiled	4 med.	48	13	1	2	tr
Mushrooms, canned, pcs.	250 ml	165	40	3	8	tr
Olives	5	20	26	tr	tr	3
Onions, chopped, raw	250 ml	169	57	2	12	tr
Peas, green, boiled	250 ml	169	142	9	26	tr
Peas, green, canned	250 ml	180	124	8	23	tr
Peppers, sweet, grn, raw	1 pepper	74	19	tr	4	tr
Potatoes, baked in skin, flesh and skin (12cm long)	1	206	225	5	52	tr
Potatoes, cooked in deep fat	10 strips	50	158	2	20	8
Potatoes, french-fried, frozen	10 strips	50	111	2	17	4
Potatoes, mashed, with milk & butter	250 ml	222	235	4	37	9
Potatoes, peeled before boiling (7cm long)	1	135	116	2	27	tr
Rutabega, boiled, drained, cubed	250 ml	180	61	2	14	tr
Spinach, boiled, drained	250 ml	190	44	6	7	tr
Squash, butternut, boiled	250 ml	254	99	3	26	tr
Squash, hubbard, boiled	250 ml	249	75	4	16	tr
Sweet Potatoes, baked, peeled	13 cm	114	117	2	28	tr
Tomato juice, canned or bottled	250 ml	258	44	2	11	tr
Tomato sauce, canned	50 ml	52	16	tr	4	tr
Tomatoes, raw	1 med.	123	23	1	5	tr
Turnips, boiled, mashed	250 ml	243	44	2	12	tr
Vegetable juice cocktail	250 ml	256	49	2	12	tr
Vegetables, mixed, canned	250 ml	172	81	4	16	tr
FRUITS AND RELATED PRODUCTS						
Apple juice, canned or bottled	250 ml	262	123	tr	31	tr
Apples, raw, with skin	1 med.	138	81	tr	21	tr
Apple sauce, canned, sweetened	250 ml	269	204	tr	54	tr
Apricots, dried, uncooked	250 ml	137	326	5	85	tr
Apricots, raw	1	36	17	tr	4	tr
Avocados, California	1	173	306	4	12	30
Bananas, raw (22cm long)	1	114	105	1	27	tr
Blueberries. raw	250 ml	153	86	1	22	tr
Cantaloup, raw, med. size	1/2	267	93	2	22	tr

FOODS LIST

	Measure	Weight (g)	Food Energy (cal)	Protein (g)	Carbohydrate (g)	Fat (g)
Cherries, sweet, raw	250 ml	153	110	2	25	1
Dates, pitted, chopped	250 ml	188	517	4	138	tr
Figs, dried, uncooked	1	19	48	tr	12	tr
Fruit cocktail, canned, water-packed	250 ml	259	83	1	22	tr
Grapefruit juice, canned unsweetened	250 ml	261	99	1	23	tr
Grapefruit, pink & red	1/2	123	37	tr	9	tr
Grapefruit, white	1/2	118	39	tr	10	tr
Grapes, Canadian type	10	24	15	tr	4	tr
Grapes, juice	250 ml	267	163	1	40	tr
Honeydew melon, raw	1/10	129	45	tr	12	tr
Kiwifruit, raw	1	91	56	tr	14	tr
Lemon, raw, without peel,	1 med.	84	24	tr	8	tr
Lemonade, frozen conc.,	355 ml	440	858	tr	225	tr
Mangos, raw, peeled	1	176	114	tr	30	tr
Nectarine, peeled	1 med.	136	67	1	16	tr
Orange juice, canned	250 ml	263	110	2	26	tr
Peaches, pared, whole	1 med.	87	37	tr	10	tr
Pears, raw with skin, med size	1	169	100	tr	26	tr
Pineapple, diced	250 ml	164	80	tr	20	tr
Pineapple juice, canned,	250 ml	264	148	tr	36	tr
Plums, raw	1 med.	66	36	tr	9	tr
Prunes, dried, uncooked	10	84	201	2	53	tr
Raisins, seedless	250 ml	174	522	6	138	tr
Raspberries, raw	250 ml	130	64	1	15	tr
Rhubarb, raw, diced	250 ml	129	27	1	6	tr
Strawberries, frozen, sweetened, sliced	250 ml	269	258	1	70	tr
Strawberries, raw, hulled	250 ml	157	47	tr	11	tr
BREAD, CEREALS AND RELATED PRODUCTS						
Crackers						
Crackers, graham	4 sqs	28	108	2	21	3
Crackers, saltines (soda)	4 sqs	11	48	tr	8	1
Breads, Rolls & Buns						
Bagel (9cm diam)	1	68	200	7	38	2
Bread, cracked wheat	1 slice	25	66	2	13	tr
Bread, melba toast	1 piece	4	16	tr	3	tr
Bread, pita (16.5cm diam)	1	60	165	6	33	1
Bread, rye, dark	1 slice	32	79	3	17	tr
Bread, white	1 slice	28	76	2	14	tr
Bread, 100% whole wheat	1 slice	25	61	3	12	tr
Bread, 60% whole wheat	1 slice	25	63	2	12	1
Buns, hamburger	1 bun	60	179	5	32	3
Buns, hot dog	1 bun	50	149	4	27	3

283

FOODS LIST

	MEASURE	WEIGHT (g)	FOOD ENERGY (cal)	PROTEIN (g)	CARBOHYDRATE (g)	FAT (g)
Croissants	1	57	235	5	27	12
English muffins	1	57	140	5	27	1
Breakfast Cereals						
Bran flakes with raisins	200 ml	42	133	3	32	tr
Bran, all bran	125 ml	45	113	5	34	tr
Corn flakes	200 ml	19	70	1	16	tr
Granola, home made	125 ml	64	312	8	35	17
Oatmeal, dry, ready	1 pouch	32	120	4	21	2
Rice Krispies	250 ml	30	112	2	25	tr
Rice, puffed	250 ml	15	59	tr	14	tr
Wheat, whole, (Shreddies)	200 ml	44	169	4	37	tr
Wheat flakes, grape nuts	200 ml	27	97	3	22	tr
CAKES						
White layer, chocolate icing (1/16 of 23cm diam cake)	1 piece	71	249	3	45	8
Fruitcake, dark (4cm x 7.5cm x 2cm)	1 slice	60	227	3	36	9
Pound cake (9cm x 8cm x 1cm)	1 slice	30	142	2	14	9
Sponge (1/12 of 22cm diam cake)	1 piece	44	131	3	24	3
White, plain (8cm x 8cm x 5cm)	1 piece	86	313	4	48	12
Cheesecake (1/12 of 23cm diam cake)	1 piece	92	278	5	26	18
COOKIES						
Brownies with nuts, home recipe	1 brownie	20	97	1	10	6
Chocolate chip, commercial (6cm diam)	2 cookies	22	104	1	15	5
Fig bars	2 bars	28	100	1	21	2
Oatmeal with raisins	2 cookies	26	117	2	19	4
Peanut butter	2 cookies	24	123	2	14	7
Short bread	2 large	28	139	2	19	6
Social Tea	2 biscuits	13	57	tr	9	2
FLOURS & GRAINS						
Cornstarch	125 ml	68	246	tr	60	0
Rice, brown, cooked	250 ml	180	214	5	46	tr
Rice, white, short grain cooked	250 ml	185	202	4	45	tr
raw	250 ml	211	766	14	170	tr
Wheat flour, all purpose	250 ml	133	484	14	101	1
PASTA						
Macaroni, enriched, cooked	250 ml	148	164	5	34	1
Noodles, egg, cooked	250 ml	169	211	7	39	2
Spaghetti, enriched, cooked	250 ml	148	164	5	34	1
SNACK FOODS						
Popcorn, air popped	250 ml	8	31	1	6	tr

FOODS LIST

	Measure	Weight (g)	Food Energy (cal)	Protein (g)	Carbohydrate (g)	Fat (g)
Potato chips	10 chips	20	105	1	10	7
Pretzels, 3 ring	1	3	12	tr	2	tr
FATS AND OILS						
Butter, tablespoon	15 ml	14	100	tr	tr	11
Corn oil	15 ml	14	124	0	0	14
Margarine with declaration of fatty acid	15 ml	14	100	tr	tr	11
Olive oil	15 ml	14	124	0	0	14
Shortening, vegetable oils	15 ml	13	117	0	0	13
Sunflower oil	15 ml	14	124	0	0	14
SALAD DRESSINGS						
Blue cheese	15 ml	16	77	tr	2	8
French	15 ml	16	64	tr	2	6
Thousand Island	15 ml	16	64	tr	3	6
SUGARS						
Brown	15 ml	9	34	0	9	0
White, granulated	15 ml	13	50	0	13	0
MISCELLANEOUS ITEMS						
Beer	341 ml	343	151	1	13	0
Coffee	250 ml	250	5	tr	1	0
Liquor, gin, rum, vodka	50 ml	47	109	0	0	0
Soft drinks, cola type	280 ml	292	120	0	30	0
Tea, beverage	250 ml	250	3	0	1	0
Wine, red table	100 ml	100	72	tr	2	0
Wine, white table	100 ml	100	68	tr	1	0
SOUPS						
Cream of mushroom, whole milk	250 ml	262	215	6	16	14
Minestrone with water added	250 ml	255	87	5	12	3
Tomato, whole	250 ml	262	170	6	24	6
Vegetable beef, water	250 ml	258	83	6	11	2
Onion	250 ml	260	29	1	5	tr

REFERENCES

Appenzeller O, Atkinson R. et al. *Sports Medicine* "Fitness, Training, Injuries"; Second Ed., Urban & Scharzenberg Baltimore-Munich 1983 (pg 71)

Bass, David H. *Your Personal Fitness Trainer* ; Ziff-Davis Press, Emeryville, California 1995

Briggs, George M. et al. *Nutrition and Physical Fitness* ; 11th Ed., Holt, Rinehart and Winston 1984

Evans, Paul Concordia *University Stingers "Strength, Conditioning and Fitness Manual"* 1988

Griffith, Winter H. *Complete Guide to Vitamins, Minerals and Supplements ;* Fisher Books 1988 (pgs. 21-74)

Hatfield, Frederick C. *Ultimate Sports Nutrition* ; Contemporary Books, Inc., Chicago, Illinois 1987.

Hermans, G.P.H. et al. *Sports Medicine and Health* "Development of a Strength Training Program" Kraemer, William J., Baechle, Thomas R. Excerpta Medica 1989 (pgs. 113-126, 68-70)

Herbert, Victor et al. *Total Nutrition "The Only Guide You'll Ever Need"*; St. Martin's Press, New York, New York 1995

Hooks, Gene *Weight Training in Athletics & Physical Education* ; Pretence Hall Inc. 1974 (pgs. 76-107)

Jayde, Negrita Nutrition *"The Truth about Carbohydrates",* Flex Magazine, August 1990 (pgs. 42-44)

Larson, David *Mayo Clinic Family Health Book* ; William Morrow and Company Inc. 1990

Lefavi, Bob *"Prioritize for Growth & Symmetry",* Muscle & Fitness Magazine, June 1991 (pgs 88-90, 175-186)

Nutrient Value of Some Common Foods, Minister of National Health and Welfare, Canada. 1980

Paris, Bob *Beyond Built* ; Warner Books, New York, New York 1991.

Ryan, Allan J. et al. *Sports Medicine "Nutrition Concerns During Training"* Bonen, Arned; Academic Press, Inc., New York 1989 (pgs. 67-76)

Sacra, Cheryl *"Fair Weather Exercisers"* , Health Magazine, May 1990 (pgs. 68-71)

Stockdale, Paula et al. *CFES Weight Training Instructor Course Level 1 "The Resource Manual"*, 2nd Ed., Canadian Fitness Education Services Ltd., Nelson, British Columbia 1988

The Encyclopedia Americana "Body Type"; International Edition, Grolier Inc.. Danbury, Connecticut, USA 1990

Whitney, Eleanor N. et al. *Understanding Nutrition,* 5th Ed.,West Publishing Company 1990

Yessis, Michael Kinesiology *"Bent-Over Laterals",* Muscle & Fitness Magazine, June 1991 (pgs. 56-58)

Yessis, Michael Kinesiology *"Deadlift",* Muscle & Fitness Magazine, October 1991 (pgs. 82-84)

Hermans, G.P.H. et al. *Sports Medicine and Health* "Development of a Strength Training Program" Kraemer, William J., Baechle, Thomas R. Excerpta Medica 1989 (pgs. 113-126, 68-70)

Other products by
Productive Fitness Products:

If you own a multi-station gym at home or you are thinking about purchasing one, **The Great Home Gym Handbook** is a must. Regardless of the type or brand of home gym, this little book covers many standard exercises common to all gyms. In addition it discusses: how to set up a program, how to care for your home gym, how to stretch, how to stay motivated and safety tips. This book is written in a clear and concise manner, with step by step instructions and photos for all exercises.

64 pages

The Great Home Gym Handbook
Canada $10.95
U.S. $8.95

The Great Home Gym Handbook covers a series of different exercises which can be performed on multi-station gyms. Each exercise description has a start and finish photo to demonstrate the proper form and positioning.

If you have a set of dumbbells at home or you are thinking about purchasing some, **The Great Dumbbell Handbook** is a must. This little book has all the different dumbbell exercises you need for working your whole body. In addition it discusses: how to set up a program, how to set up your own mini-gym, how to stretch, how to stay motivated and safety tips. This book is written in a clear and concise manner, with step by step instructions and photos for all exercises.

64 pages

The Great Dumbbell Handbook
Canada $10.95
U.S. $8.95

Dumbbell Training Poster Pack
- Four Full Color 12" x 18" Posters -
Four posters sold as a set only

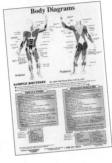

These four full color posters will make your dumbbell workouts more effective by allowing you to quickly reference proper exercise form and technique. The *Dumbbell Training* posters have all the different exercises you need for working your whole body. Fully colored muscle diagrams show you which muscles you are working. A simple "follow the steps" section will guide you through setting up your own program. Exercise descriptions are written in a clear and concise manner, with step by step instructions and photos.

Dumbbell Training Poster Pack
Canada   **$24.95**
US   **$18.95**

Call Toll-Free to Order
1-888-221-8833
or

Send cheque or money order to:
PRODUCTIVE FITNESS PRODUCTS INC.
P.O.BOX 2325
BLAINE, WA 98231-2325

30 Day Money Back Guarantee

We Accept:

Credit Cards in US Currency only

MasterCard   VISA   AMERICAN EXPRESS

The Ultimate Weight Training Journal
U.S.	$14.95	+	Shipping $4.00*
Canada	$18.95	+	Shipping $5.50*

The Great Dumbbell Handbook
U.S.	$8.95	+	Shipping $1.50*
Canada	$10.95	+	Shipping $1.50*

Dumbbell Training Poster Pack
US	$18.95	+	Shipping $4.00*
Canada	$24.95	+	Shipping $5.50*

*For two or three items combined, add only $4.50 US or $5.50 Canadian